CORAL ISLAND

MARSTON BATES *and*

DONALD P. ABBOTT

CORAL ISLAND

PORTRAIT OF AN ATOLL

Charles Scribner's Sons

NEW YORK

CONTENTS

FOREWORD 7

LIST OF ILLUSTRATIONS 10

MAPS 12

PART 1

I. *Moving In* 13

II. *Mostly About People* 25

III. *Mapping the Boondocks* 39

IV. *Fishing—and Bakalizing* 55

V. *Mostly About Food* 68

VI. *Fish Watching* 81

VII. *Radio Ifaluk* 92

VIII. *Well Digging* 105

IX. *Ship Come* 117

PART 2

X. *An End and a Beginning* 125

XI. *Mostly About Water* 132

6 *Contents*

XII. *Lagoon Interludes*   147

XIII. *Something of the Past*   164

XIV. *Fishes and Lizards*   187

XV. *The Reefs*   201

XVI. *Woleai and Tilimwol*   220

XVII. *Sialach*   235

INDEX   253

FOREWORD

IFALUK is a small dot on the map: a half a square mile of land can hardly show much detail on any scale used for Pacific distances. Further, it is spelled "Ifalik" on most maps, through some accident in the history of official spelling for place names. The people who live there call their island in a way that might be rendered "Eefahlook" in a sort of English phonetic spelling. We figure that the people who live there ought to have the final say about the name of their island: hence our divergence from the map makers.

Ifaluk is one of the Caroline Islands, which form part of Micronesia. It is some 700 miles north of New Guinea, some 400 miles south of Guam, and about 1200 miles east of the Philippines. It is a part of the Trust Territory of the Pacific Islands, administered by the government of the United States.

Ifaluk is an atoll: a roughly circular reef, built by corals and other lime-secreting organisms, marking off a quiet lagoon in the open ocean, the reef in places piled up to form islets emerging a few feet above the level of the sea. Mr. E. H. Bryan, Jr., of the Bishop Museum, in Honolulu, has compiled a list of the islands of the world that could be classed as "atolls." He finds 409: 136 in Polynesia, 92 in Micronesia, 66 in Melanesia, 15 in Indonesia, 5 northwest of Australia, 68 in the rest of the Indian Ocean, 26 in the Caribbean Sea, and only one in the Atlantic. Atoll formation, then, is primarily a phenomenon of the tropical Pacific: and the word "atoll" carries with it the connotations of warm sun, of white beaches backed by graceful palms, of friendly dark-skinned people, and of an idyllic way of life.

Ifaluk, for us, lived up to these connotations, and we found our life there a continuously rewarding experience: an experience which, in writing this book, we are trying to share.

We tested several ways of meeting the problem of joint authorship. We tried being "we" which had a nice regal sound and worked well enough when we agreed. But we have a great talent for disagreeing, despite the underlying similarity of our points of view. We tried writing in the third person—Marston did this or Don thought that—but wives, friends, editors, said this made pretty flat reading. Finally we decided to split the book: Marston Bates would write the account for the period he was on the atoll; then Donald Abbott would take over for the remaining two months. The reader can thus expect to do one mental somersault, where "I" changes from Bates to Abbott between Chapters IX and X: Bates and Ted Burrows sadly going off with the Trust Territory ship, leaving Abbott with new companions to finish the study.

It is, of course, extremely presumptuous of us—of Abbott and Bates —to write about a study that also involved five other people. But the problems of multiple authorship seem insurmountable in a non-technical book and we wanted, in any case, to write subjectively, to write about our own reactions and feelings as well as about the people and things that we observed. In a very real sense, however, all seven of us achieved a "team approach" in our study of the atoll so that, whether they like it or not, all members of the team must share some responsibility for both the observations and the thoughts that we have expressed here. And certainly there must be a total sharing of the credit for whatever good may have come out of the Ifaluk enterprise.

The Ifaluk team consisted of:

Donald P. Abbott, marine biologist, of the Hopkins Marine Station of Stanford University, on Ifaluk from June 22 to November 9, and leader of the expedition from September 12 to the end.

Theodore Arnow, geologist and hydrologist, of the U. S. Geological Survey, on Ifaluk June 22–24 and September 12–26.

Marston Bates, biologist, of the University of Michigan, on Ifaluk from June 22 to September 12.

Frederick M. Bayer, zoologist, of the U. S. National Museum, on Ifaluk from September 12 to November 9.

Edwin G. Burrows, anthropologist, of the University of Connecticut, on Ifaluk from June 22 to September 12, and leader during this time.

Robert R. Harry, ichthyologist, of the George Vanderbilt Foundation, on Ifaluk from September 12 to November 9.

Joshua I. Tracey, geologist, of the U. S. Geological Survey, on Ifaluk from September 12 to 26.

We came curiously and quickly to have a feeling of "belonging" on Ifaluk, and we found ourselves much involved with the people of the island in everything that we did. Inevitably, however, we were more closely associated with some than with others, and it may be helpful to identify here the people with whom we were most concerned, whose names appear most frequently in our narrative:

Fagolier, the paramount chief of Ifaluk.

Maroligar, the number two chief, guardian of the Fan Nap, where we lived.

Toroman, the number three chief and the official divider of food.

Lavausrung, the number four chief; a lady.

Wolpaitik, the number five chief (and the heaviest man on the island).

Totogoeiti (Tom), Ted's interpreter, and top ranking navigator (palu) of the island.

Yaniseman (Yani), "schoolteacher" and constant companion and advisor.

Bakalimar (Bakal), initially assigned as our special helper in camp and field, working later with Harry's fishing gang.

Tachiwelimeng (Tachim), neighbor, friend, and later one of Harry's fishing crew.

Letaweriur, Yani's wife and a composer of dance chants.

Gavileisei, master craftsman and canoe builder.

Gauaisig, an old man, navigator and canoe builder.

Talimeira, houseboy of Burrows and Spiro in 1948, now one of the two local "doctors."

Arueligar, "high priest" or "medicine man."

The Ifaluk study was made under the auspices of the Pacific Science Board, with a grant from the Office of Naval Research. We are particularly indebted to the Director of the Pacific Science Board, Dr. Harold J. Coolidge, and to the secretary of the Washington office, Mrs. Lenore Smith, and the secretary in Honolulu, the late Ernestine Akers, for help of all sorts.

LIST OF ILLUSTRATIONS

Photograph and chart of Ifaluk FOLLOWING PAGE 32
The Men's House
Ted Burrows relaxing
Don Abbott's English lessons

An Ifalukian house FOLLOWING PAGE 64
The census operation
Seven prominent Ifalukians
The boondocks
Collecting botanical specimens

The "ur" dance FOLLOWING PAGE 96
Making flower garlands
The Ifalukian children
Canoe building
Weaving fish nets

Ocean-going canoes FOLLOWING PAGE 128
"Rop" fishing
"Yating" fishing
Rope making

The vegetation of Ifaluk FOLLOWING PAGE 160
The women's work
Food and kitchen utensils
The scientists at work

Water profile chart FOLLOWING PAGE 192
Outer margin of reef
Marine and land life
A native fish weir
Marston Bates—photographer

Three views of Ella FOLLOWING PAGE 224
Fish from the lagoon
The women dancing
Visiting captains

1

JUNE. TO SEPTEMBER

By Marston Bates

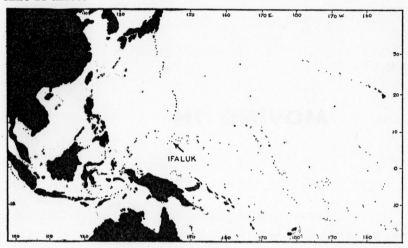

Map of the western Pacific, showing the location of Ifaluk Atoll.

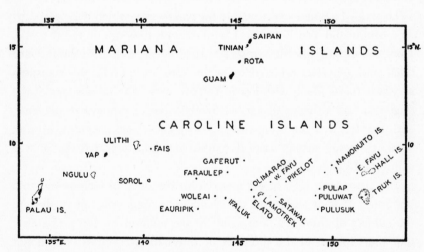

Map of the western Caroline Islands and southern Marianas, showing Ifaluk
and neighboring islands.

CHAPTER I

MOVING IN

WE SAILED from Guam at noon Saturday, June 20th, 1953, on the Coast Guard ship NETTLE. The NETTLE was an AK, an Army cargo ship converted for Coast Guard use. It displaced about 700 tons, a useful size for errands among the scattered islands of the western Pacific: large enough for ocean voyages, yet able to maneuver through the twisted passes of these reef-strewn waters. The Trust Territory Government, as well as the Coast Guard, used ships of this type.

The NETTLE had a small cabin for passengers, which was shared by Ted Arnow and Ted Burrows. I bunked with the crew in the fo'castle. Don Abbott had a berth in a sort of steel house, bolted to the forward deck, and generally referred to as the "doghouse." The ship's dispensary was there, along with berths for five men. The inhabitants of the doghouse had a theory that it was likely to fall overboard at any time, and they felt that the thing should really have been provided with an auxiliary motor, just in case. But otherwise Don reported that it was comfortable enough.

The crew were glad to get away from the dock in Guam—out into the South Seas of atolls and dusky maidens. Talk was apt to drift to the subject of these maidens, only to be checked by the probability that the captain, in the interests of international morals, would not allow shore leave. (The captain did allow shore leave and the crew, despite their talk, behaved perfectly, staying at camera-shot distance from the maidens of Ifaluk.)

It was a marvellous feeling, to be on shipboard again in a tropical

13

sea, particularly after the cramped tedium of a trans-Pacific flight, and after the tense, crowded days of final preparations for a summer out of contact with the modern world. I relaxed. I took off my shirt, to start accumulating the proper tropical color. I took off my shoes, not to wear them again until September, when respectability once more closed in on me.

We were due off Ifaluk on Monday morning. Saturday afternoon and Sunday, while the ship steamed steadily southward, we talked with each other, we napped, we talked with the sailors. We slid easily into sailor jargon, an escape from the stuffy confines of professorial dignity. We were free. We were off to see the wonderful world of the Carolines. We were off to Ifaluk, to an atoll, a coral reef, a lagoon, a fragment of Micronesia, a summer in paradise.

The planning, of course, had started many months before. As far as I was concerned, it had all started on a gray November day in Ann Arbor, with a telephone call. It was Alex Spoehr, talking from Chicago. Alex had recently resigned as Curator of Oceanic Anthropology at the Chicago Natural History Museum to take the directorship of the Bishop Museum in Honolulu and we had had several talks about possible developments in scientific research in the tropical Pacific. Alex and I shared the view that palm trees make a more attractive landscape than snow, and my envy of his shift from Chicago to Honolulu was obvious enough.

This time Alex had a concrete proposition. "How would you like to spend next summer on a Pacific atoll?"

I think I sputtered, the answer was so obvious. Alex kept on talking, sounding as though he were trying to persuade me. He was talking as a representative of the Pacific Science Board, which had a continuing program of atoll studies, and which had started work on plans for the coming year.

The official letter of invitation, from Harold Coolidge, director of the Pacific Science Board, came a few days later. It explained the background of the proposed study—the fourth of a series of intensive studies of different atolls. The atoll of Arno, in the southern Marshalls, had been studied in 1950 by a team of thirteen specialists in different sciences; Onotoa in the southern Gilberts had been investigated in 1951, by a group of six scientists; Raroia, in the Tuamotus, was the subject of study in 1952, with seven different kinds of scientists involved. It was proposed, in 1953, to work on Ifaluk, an atoll in the Western Carolines.

There were many reasons for making Ifaluk the subject of study. It was a small, self-contained unit: a half a square mile of land surface, with some 260 inhabitants, a reef surrounding a lagoon scarcely a mile in diameter, isolated in the open Pacific. In such a situation, it ought to be possible to gain some understanding of the relationships between man and nature; ought to be easier, at any rate, than with the more complex situations of large islands or parts of continents.

Ifaluk was also interesting because it had had relatively little contact with the outside world. It was too small and too remote to interest either governments or mission societies, so that the ways of the people had been little changed in recent times. The people, furthermore, had been carefully studied by two anthropologists, Edwin Burrows and Melford Spiro, who had lived on the atoll from July, 1947 to February, 1948. They had made detailed descriptions of the customs of the Ifalukians, which would provide a sound basis on which to start studies of the relations of these customs to the biological and geological conditions of the environment. Dr. Burrows would be leader of the 1953 expedition, so that it would be possible to build directly on his knowledge of the people and their language.

The supervision and coordination of these atoll studies was in the hands of the Pacific Science Board, which was a part of the National Research Council, a central coordinating agency for American scientific studies. The work was financed through a contract with the Geography Branch of the Office of Naval Research.

Why should the Navy finance general studies of Pacific Islands? The answer, I think, can be found in the American interest in the Pacific aroused during the second world war.

The Pacific had been washing the shores of the United States ever since California had become a part of the Union, but as a nation we continued to face the Atlantic and Europe. We acquired Hawaii. Somehow, in the course of our sympathy with the national aspirations of Cuba, we got tangled with the Philippines. Much earlier,

Admiral Perry had led in opening the door of Japan, and we continued to be involved in many of the maneuvers of European diplomacy in the Orient. Any catalogue of American interests and activities in the Pacific would be an impressive one—but the activities were always, somehow, offhand and secondary. We had no national consciousness of our role as a Pacific power.

Then came Pearl Harbor and the long and terrible aftermath. Never again can we look at the Pacific as an area of backyard that can be neglected or dealt with casually. We are committed to the Pacific. We must learn to live with its peoples—and for this, we must gain some understanding of their ways, their problems, and their environments. The Pacific, then, must be a continuing subject of study in our institutions of science and scholarship, a continuing preoccupation for many branches of our government. Our leaders in science and government are conscious of this; but we, as a people, must share the consciousness.

Ifaluk, certainly, is a tiny place, of no global or strategic importance. It gains significance only as an element in the grand strategy of the new American interest and responsibility in the Pacific; and perhaps also in the even grander strategy of finding ways in which the different kinds of sciences can be blended through a group approach to gain understandings of our human problems: understandings that transcend the interests of any particular science.

The plan at first was to send four people to the island for the summer: Dr. Burrows as leader and anthropologist; Don Abbott as marine biologist; me as land biologist; and Dr. J. I. Tracey of the United States Geological Survey as geologist, to study the physical structure of the atoll. It seemed unwise to inflict more than four scientists on the people—there is a limit to the amount of investigation that can be tolerated by even the most hospitable and kindly of cultures. A ratio of four investigators to a population of 260 seemed about the maximum.

We all met during Christmas vacation with scientists who had been on the previous expeditions to other atolls, to work out plans for the summer study. In the course of these discussions it became clear that something a little more ambitious might be planned. The final arrangement was that Burrows, Abbott and Bates would go out in June and stay until September, concentrating on studies of anthropology and land biology. Then Burrows and Bates would leave, so as to be able to meet their fall teaching assignments; but Abbott would stay, and the ship that came to pick up Burrows and Bates would bring four more scientists—a geologist, a hydrologist and two marine biologists.

The geologist and the hydrologist would only be able to get away from their Geological Survey duties for a few weeks; but Don Abbott and the other two marine biologists would be able to stay until November, and during this period, they would make a concentrated attack on the study of the marine environment of the atoll. All of this involved complicated logistics, since Ifaluk was not on the route of any regular shipping. It was all worked out, however, with the cooperation of the Coast Guard, the Government of the Trust Territory, and the Navy.

We met once more during the spring, in Washington, to talk about our plans. Then, on the 6th of June, Ted Burrows, Don Abbott and I met in San Francisco, flying to Honolulu together two days later.

Don was an old hand in Honolulu: he had gone to college there before the war, had been stationed there in the army during the war, and had acquired a wife there. Ted also had lived in Honolulu for many years. Only for me was it new, though curiously I had no feeling of newness. I was back in the tropics, and the lowland tropics, almost anywhere, seems like home: the familiar flowers; the warm, moist air frequently cleansed by abrupt showers; the friendly brown skins of local people; the pale angular intruders from the north, all were part of a general and well-known pattern.

We were greeted in the chilly pre-dawn by old friends of Don and Ted. Among this group was one new friend for all of us, Ernestine Akers, the secretary of the Honolulu office of the Pacific Science Board. We had been corresponding with Ernestine—about kodachrome, about tomato soup and canned spinach, about insect nets and plant presses. A problem? Ernestine would solve it, as she always did. Here she was, in person, with gorgeous leis for each of us, and a kiss as well.

We had four hectic days in Honolulu—conferences with all sorts of experts on the Pacific, last minute purchases, the inevitable paperwork of modern travel (military or otherwise), and parties. Finally we were off for Guam, by military aircraft, across the interminable Pacific, with a lunch stop at tiny Johnson Island, and a midnight stop in the rain at Kwajalein.

We were a week on Guam. We had not planned to stay that long, but when we went down to the warehouse to check the supplies that had been shipped ahead we found an enormous accumulation that seemed to include everything—except Don's special equipment. He had spent weeks gathering and packing this equipment with loving care—microscope, thermometers, jars, typewriter, apparatus for chemical tests, everything the modern marine biologist should have with him in the field. He had packed it all in steel drums so that it would be waterproof and shockproof.

A frantic exchange of cables revealed that the drums were still sitting peacefully in California—but that it might be possible to get them out by air freight. Arrangements had been made, months before, for the Coast Guard to take us from Guam to Ifaluk on June 18th, on their ship, the NETTLE. The Coast Guard officers on Guam, however, thought that departure could be delayed in view of the importance of having the equipment. So the sailing date was changed to June 20th.

We haunted the freight terminal, but no drums showed up. Don tried to face the plans of the summer without his equipment. We were able to buy some substitute materials in Guam, and to scrounge things from the local office of the Geological Survey—where Josh Tracey and Ted Arnow, who would be coming to Ifaluk in September, were stationed. Ted Arnow would be making the trip to Ifaluk with us now, but only to reconnoiter, returning to Guam with the ship. We thus also had a little time to explore Guam; but our hearts were not in it. We wanted to get to Ifaluk, to our atoll, with or without the proper equipment. We sailed without the equipment.

The NETTLE arrived off Ifaluk with dawn. Don noted the first impression in his journal. "Looked out of the port on awakening, since the ship had stopped, and there was Ifaluk—reef, lagoon, islets and all, everything a remote South Sea island should have—impossibly attractive." For Ted Arnow, Don and me, it was love at first sight. It was love for an idea, perhaps for an ideal. That's dangerous because things so rarely live up to the ideal. The miracle of Ifaluk was that it never let us down. Or maybe I should say that we were always able to fit the reality to the illusion—which remains something of a miracle, either of Ifaluk or of our minds.

For Ted Burrows it was renewal of an old love which can, in its knowledgeable way, in its uncertainties of certain change, be even more exciting. We all crowded against the rail, trying to make out the features of the separate islets, of Ella, Falalap and Falarik. The ship was anchored a couple of hundred yards off Ella, the uninhabited islet, in about twelve fathoms of water.

Don's "impossibly attractive" was partly a product of faith. There was a strong surf running, the sky was overcast, and it was cold. The first messengers from the island were flies—hordes of them that settled everywhere on the ship. Yet the cold and the flies hardly mattered. There was the rich green of the vegetation, the beach of whitened coral, and above all, the feeling of remoteness from our ordinary world —surely a concrete enough basis for the projections of any romantic mind.

Presently a single canoe came bobbing out through the swell. As the canoe came closer we could see that its occupant was a very old man, but obviously expert with the paddle. Someone threw a line to him, and he clambered over the side. Ted unlimbered the Ifalukian that he had stored from 1948, and the old man responded volubly. There was perhaps little communication, but much friendliness. This first visitor was Gauaisig, a venerable canoe builder and navigator.

Gauaisig was followed shortly by a group in a larger canoe which included Fagolier, the paramount chief, and Toteyoetin—better known as Tom—who had served as interpreter for Burrows and Spiro during their 1948 anthropological study. Soon the ship was surrounded by canoes and the decks populated with Ifalukians.

With Tom aboard, the line of communication was established. Tom, in his youth, had somehow escaped the island, working on ships from Singapore to Honolulu, and living for a stretch of six years in Manila. He learned, in these wanderings, a sort of English—not pidgin, but a special, Tom variety, of the language. Ted Burrows and Tom understood one another easily; I never was able to get much idea of what

Tom might be talking about. But I could talk to Ted, Ted to Tom, and Tom to any Ifalukian.

Ted Burrows, as chief of the expeditionary party, went ashore with Tom and Fagolier, the chief of Ifaluk, to continue the preliminaries of greeting and to arrange for setting up camp. Ted Arnow, since he would have only the two days here to arrange for his wells for water level studies, left soon after in a smaller canoe, to start reconnoitering. Don and I stayed on the NETTLE all morning, our impatience to get ashore tempered by the wind, the intermittent rain, and the cold.

The sky cleared after lunch, and we went ashore in the ship's launch: riding the high swell of the pass into the calm, clear water of the lagoon. The launch approached shore with some caution, finding its way among the coral heads to ground on the smooth coral sand. Shoes off, passengers and crew jumped overboard to wade the last few feet to the beach. Crossing the beach, we passed abruptly from the blazing sun into the cool half-shade of a neatly maintained park of coconut palms.

We walked on to the Men's House, the Fan Nap, a big, high-gabled, rectangular thatched structure, some forty yards in from the lagoon shore, in the palm grove. Ted and the chiefs were sitting on the temple grass outside, deep in arrangements for the establishment of camp. Ted and Spiro, during their 1948 stay, had lived in tents, but they had found the thatched houses of the island much more comfortable. This time the chiefs, at Ted's request, turned the Fan Nap over to us. And a very satisfactory residence it proved to be. This must have caused some inconvenience to the men of the island, but there were five big canoe houses along the lagoon shore and these, too, served as clubs. The important business of the island continued to be transacted around the Fan Nap, but on the lawn outside while we were in residence.

Don and I squatted for a while on the fringe of the conference between Ted and the chiefs, exchanging grins with the other onlookers. But we didn't stay long because of the flies. There were incredible numbers of flies of a half-dozen assorted sizes, slight variations on the common or garden house-fly type. We never got used to them— but neither did the Ifalukians, who generally carried a small branch around with them to serve as a fly switch.

While we were making these first explorations of our new environment, Captain Cowart of the NETTLE surveyed the pass into the lagoon and marked the treacherous coral heads with buoys made from large gasoline drums painted orange. The sea was still running too high for the NETTLE to risk trying the passage into the lagoon, so all of us went back aboard and the ship hauled anchor to spend the night slowly cruising in circles some miles off shore.

Next day the sea was calm, and Captain Cowart, with great skill, slowly maneuvered the NETTLE between the coral heads of the pass into the lagoon. He anchored off the Fan Nap and the launch plied back and forth all morning unloading the supplies for the summer. There was an appalling amount of stuff; provisions calculated for seventeen man-months since there would be three people for three months, five people for almost another month, and three people again for still another month. Besides the food—the cases of tomato juice and dried prunes and sauerkraut and corned beef and crabmeat—there was special equipment for each of the seven different kinds of scientists involved in the total project. No, not seven, because Don's drums were missing. Don, looking at the growing mountain on the beach, and still mourning those missing drums, figured his stuff would have been less than three per cent of the total—if it had been there.

I was somewhat unsympathetic about this, subscribing to the theory that the naturalist with notebook, pencil, an open mind and perhaps a hand lens, was well equipped. My theory worked well—as long as my colleagues ignored it in planning, so that I could scrounge on them. As I did, all that summer.

Ted and I struggled all day trying to keep some sort of order among the endless cases, drums, trunks, cartons and boxes that were unloaded from the NETTLE. Don and Arnow, in the meanwhile, explored the island to determine where wells should be dug for a study of the distribution of fresh water under the atoll. Don would be supervising the digging of the wells and it was important that he have a clear idea of what Arnow wanted.

Everyone went back to the NETTLE for supper and to spend the night. Captain Cowart, through Tom, had invited all of the island people to come aboard for a movie that night. About dusk, they started to appear—small canoes, large canoes, by the dozens, each completely packed with men, women, kids and babes in arms. It seemed hardly possible that any of the 260 inhabitants of the island could be missing.

There was terrific confusion, but somehow the chief bosun's mate managed to keep the confusion within some sort of bounds, helping the ladies overside, passing the babies from hand to hand, keeping the unloading canoes from blocking access to the gangway. The people accumulated on the foredeck, where the screen had been set up, and this presently was packed solid with chattering, brown, naked humanity.

The movie was pretty bad, even as ship's movies go. The Captain had given considerable thought to the selection, the important things being to have color and plenty of noise. It was a "comedy" set in Texas, with night clubs, round-ups, brawls—lots of action, lots of color, lots of noise and no discernible plot or meaning for a European or anyone else. But the audience enjoyed it hugely.

Near the end a drizzle set in and confusion mounted again as the assemblage started to disperse. Confusion had really never ceased, as people arrived and left all during the show, but it reached a climax with the mass exodus. We watched the process from the bridge where we could look down into the bright circle of light made by the big lamps over the gangway. We counted fourteen people packed into the little rowboat we had brought along, borrowed from the trader, Bronson, in Guam. This had been pressed into service along with all of the canoes of the island. There seemed hardly an inch of freeboard. But what with the calmness of the lagoon and the skill of the Ifalukians (and the patience of the supervising members of the NETTLE crew) the debarkation was accomplished without incident.

When quiet had settled again, the rest of the movie was run off for the benefit of the crew, who wanted to see how it came out. Ted Burrows and I—always conscious of our well-advertised need for long hours of sleep—went off to our respective bunks, while Don and Ted Arnow settled down in the messroom to talk for half the night about the study plans.

Burrows and Abbott and I had had plenty of time to talk about plans during the flight out from the States and the wait in Guam, and there

had also been opportunity at the preliminary conferences for exchange of ideas with Bayer and Rofen. There had been less chance for
talk with Arnow and Tracey who, as hydrologist and geologist respectively, would have a basic part in any unified approach to the problems
of the atoll environment. Water, soils, the physical structure of the reef
and the emergent islets, these were the special interests of Arnow and
Tracey, and both had a large fund of experience in the western Pacific
—something that Don and I lacked completely.

Ted Arnow bore the label "hydrologist"—a student of water. Water
is remarkable stuff, and the whole development of life on this planet
is tied up with its behavior and properties. Hydrologists, of course, are
mostly concerned only with the physical aspects of water—its storage
and flow and cycling through the processes of weather. But whatever
may be the characteristics of hydrologists in general, Ted Arnow's interests ranged out widely from this, to cover the whole of the environment in which he was living or working. He and Don, as the night
drifted on and the conversation wandered from reefs to plants to water-
levels to the food habits and customs of the Micronesians, found no
sharp points of disagreement, but rather a general sharing of points of
view and interests that augured well for the success of the collaboration.

The next day was Wednesday, the 24th of June. The last of the gear
was put ashore in the morning. Again Ted Arnow and Don explored
the island paths to work out the strategy of water study, while Ted
Burrows and I struggled to get some order in the piles of supplies.
Captain Cowart surveyed the lagoon to see whether it would be practical for seaplane landing. Since the longest clear, straight run was
hardly a mile, take-off there with a craft of any size would not be
practical.

We went back to the NETTLE again for lunch. In the afternoon we
started to concentrate on camp arrangements in earnest: poring over
the lists to find the cases with the stove, the cots, the cooking utensils;
arranging tables, and trying to stack the food reserve so that the most
essential items would be somewhat accessible. We put up a large
tent beside the Fan Nap to store things that would not be immediately

useful—though of course we spent a deal of time in the next days re-arranging these piles to get at something at the bottom that was needed at once.

Finally, with the last launch, Ted Arnow went back aboard, re-gretfully but cheered by his glimpse of the possibilities for study that would await him when he returned in September. The rest of us, with a good part of the local population, squatted on the coral sand of the lagoon beach and watched the NETTLE slowly edge its way through the pass of the lagoon out to the open sea.

We were saying good-bye to the Western world for the summer, and it seemed a good riddance. No mail, no telephone, no communica-tion of any kind except the arrangements that on September 12th, a ship belonging to the Trust Territory would come to pick up Ted and me, and to leave Josh Tracey, Ted Arnow, Ted Bayer and Bob Rofen for the last period of the projected study. The Navy had provided a "Gib-son Girl" radio for emergency use; and there was a plan that the air-plane on weather patrol would occasionally circle the island to be sure everything was all right. But these arrangements for contact seemed remote and unimportant, at most a vague reassurance for some im-probable catastrophe. How could there be a catastrophe on this sunny island, with these delightful people?

We had become curiously fond of the NETTLE and her crew, con-sidering how short, really, the association had been. But we still were glad to see her go, and to look forward to the peace of an unmechanized summer.

CHAPTER II

MOSTLY ABOUT PEOPLE

THURSDAY, the first day after the NETTLE left, was over-cast, with occasional drizzling rains. This was probably just as well because it cut down on the temptation to wander; so we could concentrate on the organization of camp at the Fan Nap.

The Fan Nap—the "Men's House"—was a large structure, some forty feet long and twenty wide, with a high thatched roof that sloped steeply to within a couple of feet of the ground on the sides. The ends were closed with matting down to within four feet of the ground, which meant that any adult must crouch on entering or leaving. The main cross-beams inside were higher, but still low enough to be a constant hazard. I never did learn to use the proper inside-of-house crouch, and kept battering my head all summer. Ted and Don were more alert—or at least better at dodging.

The front part of the Fan Nap, nearest the lagoon, was used for sleeping quarters. Ted and Don had their cots at the sides, under the stringers—beams that had been hewn out of huge breadfruit logs. The logs looked precariously balanced on the heavy coral blocks that served as the corner posts of the house. Collapse of the house would have caused the occupants of the cots to be instantly crushed. The great beams, so close above, were thus at first something of a mental hazard. But they had withstood the gales of many years and were clearly solidly placed—and they were very convenient for hanging mosquito nets.

Tables and boxes were arranged in the central area to make working space. The equipment included carpenter's tools, and with these some of the wooden packing boxes were converted into sets of shelves. The cases of food were piled along the sides in the back part of the house, which became the kitchen area, cozily walled with cartons of sliced peaches and spam.

There was an altar in the back part of the Fan Nap that was a constant mental hazard because we did not want to offend the local people by desecrating this shrine with profane objects. The altar was a ramshackle affair, contrasting strongly with the usual Ifalukian workmanship, and this may have indicated that it was not taken very seriously; but we wanted to run no risk of giving offense. There was a large chest there, too, which we judged to be a sort of depository for the appurtenances of government. Among other things, the American flag was stored in the chest, to be hauled out and attached to a pole on the lagoon shore when a ship was sighted.

There was another sacred touch to the Fan Nap—a phallus attached to the main front center post and pointing out across the lagoon. The phallus, which pointed westward toward Woleai, the nearest neighboring atoll, commemorated an event of Ifaluk legend—or history. The story was one of violence and conquest and seemed curiously anomalous in the Ifalukian folklore, contrasting as it did with the present completely non-aggressive and peaceful character of the people. Ted thought that it might reflect memories of an actual conquest by the people of Ifaluk of earlier inhabitants of the neighboring atolls. Maur, the main character in the legend, was certainly the "culture hero" of the people of the island.

The phallus did not seem to be the object of any special veneration or cult—it was just there. Once, later in the summer, when we were trying to explain the money system of the United States, we were questioned about the portrait heads on the coins. Don explained Washington and Lincoln as long-dead "chiefs" thus commemorated.

Yani got the idea at once. "Ifaluk have picture of dead chief, too," he said, grinning, as he pointed toward the phallus of Maur on the Fan Nap.

The weather continued to interfere with the starting of field work. Friday it rained almost continuously all day—and of course the rain gauge wasn't unpacked and set up yet. A stiff wind came up in the afternoon and kept increasing in force. Late in the afternoon Tom came by with Maroligar, the number two chief. Tom pointed out across the lagoon to the west and said, "Maybe typhoon." Maroligar seemed somewhat worried as well. What the two wanted, apparently, was a weather prediction—from us newcomers to the tropical Pacific! It showed a touching and completely misplaced faith in the famous "American know-how." I was in charge of the meteorology department and I peered at the thermometer (79°F at 5:45 P.M.) and barometer (1005 millibars) but I was unable to draw any deductions from these helpful facts.

In the evening, quite a number of men gathered in back of the Fan Nap, clearly worried about the weather. Maroligar borrowed one of the big Navy battery flashlamps and learned how to turn it on and off. He wanted some sort of a light so that if the weather worsened during the night, he could round everyone up and lead them to some safer spot, perhaps the boulder ridge on the windward side of the island—the highest spot, some fifteen feet above sea level. The houses were mostly along the lagoon shore and Ted remembered that waves had reached to the Fan Nap on his previous stay, with a wind of considerably less than typhoon violence. Don and I read what there was on typhoons in the books we had brought along, and I tried to remember what I could about the characteristics of Caribbean hurricanes—but nothing helpful came out of this.

The wind settled down to a steady blow, and I comforted myself, going to sleep, by thinking that hurricanes struck suddenly, after a period of still, oppressive heat, so that this slow build-up of wind could hardly be dangerous—misinformation, but none-the-less comforting.

The next day, Saturday, started out cold, with a completely overcast sky. But the rain had let up, so we sallied forth to begin work. Our first project was to make a census of the people on the island. Ted had made a census on his 1948 visit and he wanted to get a record of the changes. For Don and me, the census would be an essential basis for our studies of "human ecology." Further, if we made the census our first item of business, it would give us an opportunity to meet all of the people on the island.

Ted, of course, was in charge of the census operation. Tom acted as interpreter. Fagolier, the paramount chief, and Maroligar, the number two chief, went along, giving the highest possible official sanction to the procedure. The party also included a young man named Bakalimar—shortened to Bakal for ordinary purposes—who had been assigned by the chiefs to work with us, acting as general handyman and, most importantly, as dishwasher. (We did our own cooking; or, perhaps more accurately, our own can-opening.)

We were also accompanied by Tony. Tony was from the atoll of Ulithi, some 375 miles northwest of Ifaluk. He was a young man of perhaps eighteen, and had come to Ifaluk with his younger brother on the trade ship, some months before our arrival, to visit relatives. The Coast Guard had a station on Ulithi, where Tony had worked, and where he had learned fluent English. He was of no use as an interpreter in the census operation, however, because of his lack of familiarity with the Ifaluk household and clan arrangements, and because his youth made the questioning seem almost impertinent. The job required the maturity, dignity and local knowledge possessed by Tom. Tony's name, Antonio, was official, because Ulithi had been converted by a Roman Catholic Mission some years earlier—a process that included the adoption of Christian names.

The houses of Ifaluk were all on the two largest islets of the atoll, Falalap and Falarik, which were separated by a shallow and rather narrow pass. The Fan Nap, near the southern end of Falarik, was roughly in the center of the inhabited area. We started the census with the southernmost houses of Falalap, with the idea of working gradually northward until the count, household by household, was finished.

Three households—twenty-six people—were catalogued that first morning. Tom and Ted would lead the way into a household area, going inside if it was drizzling, or sitting on mats in the open during dry intervals. The available people of the household would gather about— and the available people included all of the men, all of the children except those who got scared at the strange activity and ran away, and all of the women except those under temporary quarantine in a menstrual hut.

Menstruating women on Ifaluk, as in many cultures, were subject to a variety of taboos. There were four special houses on the atoll which served as menstrual huts for each of the four villages into which the households were grouped. A woman, at the onset of menstruation, retired to one of these, removed from the ordinary life of the community until her period was over.

The census-taking was not a rapid process. It took interminable palavering among Tom, the chiefs and the members of each household to get a list of names, with clan affiliations, marital status, and such-like lore dear to the anthropological heart. When the list was complete, Don supervised the weighing and taking of heights—the only physical measurements practical with the available equipment. The weights were taken on a set of ordinary bathroom scales that had been picked up in Guam. The measuring pole was less prosaic—made from a pole found in the Fan Nap and calibrated to the nearest quarter inch by marking with a ball-point pen. Maroligar officiated at the weighing and measuring; after he had watched the first two or three operations, he explained to each person where to put his feet on the scales, tried to persuade him to stand up straight for the measuring, and coaxed the shier women and children into cooperating.

In the meantime I would prowl around with the big Crown Graphic camera, snapping whatever caught my interest, and popping flash-bulbs to the delight of the children who had a new toy in the used bulbs.

There was plenty of time to look around while Ted was trying to get all of the names and relationships straight. We noticed that the houses were well built, with big posts stuck in the ground to which stringers and rafters were firmly lashed with stout coconut-fiber rope; the roofs were coconut thatch, and the walls were mats woven of coconut leaves. The houses were low, and people did not stand in them, but sat or sprawled on the floor, which was very clean and covered with plaited coconut mats. There were no windows as such, but each house had four to six doors, which could be closed with more coconut mats when desired. The interiors were dim—but there was no need for good reading light. There was little or no clutter on the floor, except for a few things propped against the walls. Most of the family possessions were put in bags or boxes of various sorts and slung by ropes from the rafters, the whole upper part of the house thus being a sort of floorless attic.

The citizens of Ifaluk cooperated nicely in the census operation, though they seemed rather amused at such strange antics. Those who had been weighed and measured loved to stand around and watch the rest as they passed through the routine. It was hard to get some of the people, especially the women, to stand up straight enough for a proper height measurement. They had, in many cases, what seemed to be a permanent crouch, perhaps resulting from the low doorways and interiors, perhaps the product of a sort of chronic deference, since the women of Ifaluk knew their place—always bowing respectfully in the presence of the male animal. (Ted suspected that this show was superficial and that the women, there as everywhere, knew their power and how to use it; one of the five chiefs, it turned out, was a woman.)

There were no ideas of modesty associated with the breasts; and the ladies didn't seem to be bothered by the fact that their skirts gaped rather badly near the belt-line behind. But they were very modest about legs from the knee up and were careful never to expose an inch of thigh. Their preoccupation with keeping their skirts close about their legs was clear enough as they stepped on the scales. Don, impressed by their modest maneuvers as he tried to read the dial on the scales, remarked that they would really be shocked by an American bathing suit.

The people seemed to take wonderful care of the children, the men holding babies and comforting the young as often as the women. Ted and his colleague, Spiro, in their 1948 study, found that the kids were never spanked, and rarely yelled at—though it was said that they sometimes doused them in the lagoon if they got too obstreperous. At the movies on the NETTLE Don noticed one man gently ladling sea water on a bawling baby. The baby stopped crying quickly—and he made a mental note to try this on his own daughter when he got back home.

The smallest infants were in cradles. These were square boxes with low sides, fastened by a bridle of cords from the corners, and suspended a few inches above the floor by a rope from the rafters. The babies were tucked in with some old clothes, and seemed contented enough.

In general, the people had fine physiques, and seemed very healthy. There was one woman who looked like an albino with freckles, and another old woman had her nose and upper lip completely eroded away, probably from yaws. Yaws was once prevalent in all of these islands, but it yields quickly to penicillin injections and during the post-war period of American control, the Navy medical service instituted an effective campaign of yaws control.

After the first three households had been completed, the party waded back across the shallow pass to "home" at the Fan Nap for lunch. The weather kept us in for the rest of the day. The sky had been completely overcast all morning, with occasional drizzling rains, but without strong wind. In the afternoon the wind became steadily stronger. It started to tear coconut fronds, even green ones, from the trees, and the coconuts themselves were being blown off in large numbers. Don noticed one coconut fall at an angle of about thirty degrees from the vertical in the wind, and he figured that the wind had the force of eight or nine on the Beaufort scale—gale force.

About four o'clock Maroligar and some other men came around to the Fan Nap and lashed poles and boards across the open western end, where it faced the lagoon. A tent that had been unpacked but not set up was dragged over and lashed to the poles, nicely cutting out the wind and rain and making the interior fairly snug and comfortable. But the noise of the wind and waves outside kept increasing. A typewriter could not be heard four feet away, even in this snug interior. (Ted was typing up his notes from the morning, impervious to typhoons.)

We kept worried eyes on the barometer and on the wildly swaying palms. Men everywhere were out battening down their house walls with matting, and running great ropes from the gables, making them fast to the bases of nearby palms. Maroligar, hovering about the Fan Nap with obvious concern about the guests on the island, made it clear that if things got much worse we should move in to one of the houses farther from the shore.

Then suddenly, about five o'clock, the worryings and speculations were disrupted by a wave of excitement. An airplane had been sighted circling the atoll! Everyone rushed out to see. Don and I dashed back to the Fan Nap to get the walkie-talkies that had been provided for just this sort of a situation. The walkie-talkies had not been tested since being unpacked, but there was no time now. Don's seemed to transmit all right, but neither was very clear as a receiver, at least in the howling gale, so I ran back to the Fan Nap to tune the battery receiver-set there on the walkie-talkie wave length.

Don gave his position on the lagoon shore near the south end of the long island, and the plane must have heard because it turned and made a pass almost directly overhead. It was a weather observation plane from Guam. At the receiver set, with Ifaluk crowded around me, I could hear the whole conversation.

"Any damage there? Any damage there? Over."

"No damage, nobody hurt. Wind about Beaufort Nine. Is a typhoon coming? Over."

"Typhoon center already past now north of Ifaluk and moving northwest. Wind now at maximum velocity. We will report to Guam that you are all right . . ."

The plane disappeared into the mist over the north end of Falarik and out of radio range. Don lingered on the beach to make sure it would not make another circle, and I kept my ear at the radio for any further message, but only static came through. But we had heard enough. No more typhoon. Science said so. Western civilization had zoomed in from the sky to reassure us—and the relief was immense.

We relayed the information to the chiefs. Ifaluk was tremendously impressed with the whole business—the appearance of the plane, the conversation with the little boxes, and pick-up of the conversation on the Zenith radio in the Fan Nap. Goodness knows, we were impressed too.

Weeks later, when the trade ship of the Trust Territory Government stopped by Ifaluk, we found out that the storm had gained in force as it moved northwest and had hit the atoll of Ulithi squarely. Father William J. Walter, the missionary on Ulithi, described the damage in a letter to Don:

"A few hundred trees were uprooted and a few hundred more snapped in half. Paths were so strewn with debris that they were

IFALUK ATOLL

From a Japanese sketch survey in 1921
Ifalik I. s, Lat 7°14' 57' N., Long 144°27' 01' E.

Natural Scale 1:50,000

Falarik I.

Elangalap I.

Ella I.

Falalap I.

Nautical Miles

Meters

ABOVE Ifaluk is an atoll: a roughly circular reef marking off a quiet lagoon in the open ocean.

INSERT Ifaluk Atoll, as it appears on U. S. Navy Hydrographic Office chart H. O. 5425. Atoll and island names have been changed to conform to present usage on the atoll.

BELOW The chiefs turned the Fan Nap, the Men's House, over to us for our residence.

ABOVE Cases of food walled the kitchen area: Ted Burrows sometimes propped himself cozily there to read at night.

BELOW Don proposed a trade of English lessons for lessons in Ifalukian.

obliterated completely. The ferocious wind scooped up the sea and hurled it over the island, ruining the fresh water in our rain catchments. The waves came up into the canoe houses and crumpled some of them. All canoes had previously been dragged inland into the villages and tied down between the houses. One of the women's club houses, which also served as maternity ward and hospital, began swaying under the impact of the storm. The women and children were removed to safety just before it disappeared in a spray of flying splinters. The waves piled up and crashed on the beach rolling water a hundred yards inland. The islands are only ten feet above sea level and the ocean threatened to inundate the land. All the coconuts and most of the fronds had been stripped from the trees. For nine months afterwards the people were on short rations and no copra could be produced."

The same trade ship brought news that another storm, about a month before, had hit Ulithi when a fleet of fishing canoes was out on the reef. Three canoes, with seven men, disappeared. The lost men included Tony's uncle, brother and nephew, and his niece lost her husband.

Ifaluk was too close to the equator to be often in the path of typhoons; it was in the area where these storms generally build up, gaining hurricane force as they move north. The island had not been struck by a major typhoon since 1907, but the storm of that year was a fearful one, and its mark was still on the island. From the lagoon, a few coconut palms stood out, much taller than the others; they were the survivors of the 1907 disaster. Great blocks of coral tossed up on the reef before Falalap were testimony enough to the unbelievable force of the sea.

The wind continued, but it could be ignored now that it held no threat of increased violence, and in the evening Don and I started seriously on our project of learning something about the language of Ifaluk. We had asked one of the young men, Yaniseman, to help with this, and he turned up with his good friend Tachiwelimeng.

This was the beginning of a close friendship and constant collaboration. Yaniseman was one of three young men from the island who had been sent to Yap for several months by the government of the Trust Territory to learn English and, on return, to serve as teachers for the island. The English that they could learn in this time was rudimentary, but they were anxious to learn more. Don proposed a sort of trade with Yani of English lessons for Ifaluk lessons. This developed presently into a regular session, every second or third night, with about a dozen of the young men of the island in attendance. I soon dropped out. The English-Ifalukian exchange thus became Don's enterprise: he had a special interest, since he would be staying on after Ted and I left.

By next morning (Sunday) the wind had pretty much died down, and the census operation was continued. About noon, a Navy ship was sighted off Falarik. The walkie-talkies were again unlimbered and contact was established. It turned out to be a destroyer escort, calling by the island to check typhoon damage. They sent in a rubber landing boat with a half a dozen men who spent about an hour wandering around the island trading cigarettes for shells, and then took off. It began to look as though Ifaluk, instead of being isolated in the remote Pacific, was a busy crossroads.

Monday, Tuesday, Wednesday, and finally the census was completed —or at least the first draft of the census. We made out a detailed list of all of the people, household by household, with a copy for each of us, and we kept making small changes all summer, finally making a complete recheck at the end of the summer to be sure we had everything straight. When I think of the trouble we had keeping track of 260 people, I get a new insight into the problem of census operations in a country like the United States. "Census" will never again be just a word.

The Ifalukians did not count years, and consequently did not know exactly how old they were. They did, however, have a series of words for age groups: saugau for infant, sari for child, tarimwan for young man, liveirik for a girl past puberty, and so forth. Old men and old women were called tufai and there were a number of old people on the island: twenty-eight men and thirty women in the tufai class, to be exact, so that about a third of the population was in the old age group. Some of these, including Tom, were adults at the time of the 1907 typhoon, so that they must have been in their sixties at the time of our visit: but they were healthy, vigorous and obviously enjoying life.

Ted asked each woman of childbearing age how many children she had had, how many were still living, and—for those that had died—

whether they died in infancy (before they could walk) or later. The ninety-two women of childbearing age or older had had 255 children, of which 151 were still living. Of the 104 deaths, sixty were either still-births or infant deaths, which is a high infant mortality by modern Western standards, though probably lower than that of most of the crowded Oriental civilizations.

The menstrual history of every woman was public knowledge on Ifaluk because of the custom of retiring to the menstrual huts. Tufai for a woman, then, has the definite meaning that she has passed menopause, has completed her reproductive history. We got the reproductive history of twenty-eight of these elderly ladies. They had born a total of eighty children, or an average of 2.8 each. Eight of them had had no children; one of them had had ten; most had had two, three or four.

The Ifalukians, like most people who lack a written language or system of records, had amazing memories, and I think that our histories for these women are reasonably accurate. It is difficult to interpret them precisely, of course, because of our lack of data on movement to and away from the island, and the like. Clearly, however, the population is hardly maintaining itself. The Ifalukians loved children, seemed always to want children. I could not, however, get away from a suspicion that the low birth rate reflected some sort of deliberate contraceptive or control practice, beyond such conventional taboos as the prohibition of sexual intercourse during periods of fishing. The language problem, the delicacy of the subject and our reluctance to appear to be prying into personal matters, prevented us from getting any definite information.

The population question in the Pacific is a matter of general concern. All of the islands—Polynesian, Micronesian, Melanesian—showed a great decline in population through the 19th century. The islands had probably been almost free of contagious disease before the explorers, traders, whalers and other Westerners started roaming the Pacific, bringing smallpox, measles, venereal diseases, tuberculosis and the like along with them.

The consequences were devastating, and only in recent years have introduced medicine and sanitation started to counteract the effect of the introduced diseases. Until quite recently, I suspect that most cultural changes brought by the West—changes in clothing, in housing, in diet, in customs—have tended to increase the disease problem rather than to alleviate it. But that is a pet peeve of mine.

The population history of Ifaluk itself is not clear. Counts by anthropologists during the period of German control showed populations of 281 in 1903 and 208 in 1909, with an estimate of 300 for 1914. The drop between the first two counts may be a result of the typhoon of 1907—not only direct mortality, but also emigration to other islands as a consequence of food shortage.

The older Ifalukians thought that more people had lived on the island formerly; and from their stories I got to thinking that the population might at some time have reached as much as 500. This was based on accounts of times when even coconuts were carefully shared and nothing was wasted. Abandoned household sites in the village areas might be evidence of some population decline and there were stories of an epidemic, soon after the Japanese appeared, when as many as a dozen people died in a day. This, clearly, was smallpox; and the Japanese started vaccination, which has been maintained by the American authorities.

The island, in 1953, was not overpopulated. The land surface of the atoll was about a half a square mile, so the population of 260 people would represent a density of about 520 persons per square mile: a rather dense population, but we must remember that the people of Ifaluk had also the resources of their lagoon and of the surrounding seas. Ifaluk seemed to me to represent an economy of abundance, and this probably in part explains the idyllic living conditions that prevailed. With more people, with the same resources and the same cultural equipment, life might have been more difficult and unpleasant.

The Ifalukians certainly seemed not only happy, but healthy. It is difficult to make exact comparisons between the Ifalukians and other people because of our uncertainty about precise ages, so that one is likely to be averaging fifteen-year-olds with thirty-year-olds. In general, however, the men seemed to be somewhat smaller and lighter than the American average. The tallest man of the island, Sepemal, was a half inch under six feet. The heaviest (Wolpaitig, the number five chief) weighed 182 pounds with a height of 5′ 7½″. Wolpaitig came closest of any man on the island to having a paunch.

The women were considerably more under American averages for height or weight. They were generally only an inch or so over or under five feet, weighing not much over a hundred pounds. The heaviest, a matron named Ietili of the Garotrong household, weighed 150 pounds, and was 5′ 1½″ tall. Ted suspected that the small size and light weight of the women was a consequence of the fact that they carried out the regular toil of the island—the heavy gardening work of the taro swamps as well as the work around the houses.

The Ifalukians would be classed as Micronesians: but what that means is anybody's guess. "Micronesia" is a geographical term to cover the hundreds of "tiny islands" of the Marianas, the Carolines, the Marshalls and the Gilberts. The inhabitants of these island groups, the Micronesians, are hardly to be distinguished from the more famous Polynesians: a rapid survey of several anthropology texts shows that the two are more often classed together than not. The inhabitants of the various island groups of Micronesia are certainly more diverse, both culturally and physically, than the inhabitants of Polynesia: but the similarities among all of these light-skinned people of the Pacific are greater than their differences. And the problem of the origin and history of the Ifalukians, of the Caroline Islanders, of the Micronesians, cannot be separated from the much-discussed problem of the origin of the Polynesians.

I think part of the European fascination with Polynesia (which would apply equally to the people of the central Carolines) comes from the fact that these people look very much like ourselves. The features of the Ifalukians were very European, and I amused myself by noting resemblances in certain individuals, in features or apparent characters, to particular friends or acquaintances in the States. The people were not really dark-skinned: both Don and I acquired a skin color within a month that matched the Ifalukian average, as determined by frequent comparisons of arms placed side by side. A pair of naked legs walking by the Fan Nap, observed under the low over-hang of thatch, could not be identified as Ifalukian or American. The Ifalukians were surely as mixed up racially as the Europeans (none of us can afford to be stuffy about purity of race) but the mixture in the Ifalukians must have contained some of the same elements as the European mixture. But how did they get so far away?

Most anthropologists believe that the Pacific islanders moved out from southeast Asia, perhaps around the beginning of the Christian era, when the inhabitants of southeast Asia may have had a larger "Caucasian" component in their racial mixture than now. Despite his daring feat with the Kon-Tiki, few experts have much faith in Thor Heyerdahl's theory of American origin: he certainly proved that cross-Pacific contact is possible, but the evidence of language, culture and race points overwhelmingly to a Malayasian origin. One of the more probable migration routes for the Polynesians is from southeast Asia to the Philippines and through the Caroline islands to the central and south Pacific.

One gets the feeling, in this Polynesian-Micronesian area, of dealing with cultures far more complex than the technology would indicate: of dealing with the remnants of a high culture, of a "civilization." One feels that these same people, with the resources of a continent, could have built Angkor Vat or Copan: and they did produce some spectacular carving and building in places like Ponape and Easter Island. It is easy to understand the lure of the search for some "lost civilization" to account for these cultures; to understand the desire to create a mid-Pacific "continent of Mu" after the fashion of Atlantis. Maybe there is a general human tendency to explain the fascinating with the fabulous. Certainly the Pacific islanders are fascinating enough; but they have given us very few clear clues to either their origin or their history, and the few clues that we have are in part conflicting. Probably we shall never arrive at a clear and unequivocal reconstruction of their past.

But we were absorbed with the Present on Ifaluk. We had not yet acquired a proper Ifalukian shade of brown when we finally managed to finish our census of the people: but even with our strange color, we had already begun to feel at home, to feel "Micronesian" ourselves, a part of the island.

CHAPTER III

MAPPING
THE BOONDOCKS

THE IDEA was to study the human ecology of Ifaluk: the interrelations of man, his culture, and the environment. For man and his culture there was the reservoir of information accumulated by Burrows and Spiro during their 1948 residence on the island: studies which Ted planned to continue during his second visit. Don and I, with the enthusiasm of amateurs, wanted to help in this anthropological work. But there was also the environment to be studied—the land, the reef, the lagoon, the sea, the plants and animals. This "simple" situation—260 people living on half of a square mile of coral rock and sand—was incredibly complex.

When we had finished the counting, weighing and measuring of *Homo sapiens,* the next step seemed to be a start with the environment. The logical first move here was a map, a topographic survey of the situation.

The map problem was greatly simplified by the fact that a little previously a Navy reconnaissance plane had made a series of vertical and oblique aerial photographs of the whole atoll. The Ifalukians were fascinated by these photographs. They seemed to have no trouble at all in grasping the significance of either the vertical or oblique shots, and most people easily recognized the major landmarks, even locating their particular family dwellings. They knew the atoll thoroughly, and the aerial photographs gave them a chance to stand off and look at the whole thing at once, for the first time.

Don and I spent one morning drawing a base map for the island of Falarik from a mosaic of the vertical air photographs. With this outline, the next problem was to fill in details of trails, households and vegetation. We thought we would start by mapping the principal trails.

Both of us were rank amateurs at sketch mapping. We had a Brompton compass lent by Ted Arnow and a triangular ruler marked with conventional scales, but no measuring tape more than six feet long and no plane table.

We first tried improvising a tape by tying knots at two-yard intervals in 100 yards of cod-line. When we had finished this tedious job, we discovered the darn thing stretched and tangled too easily to be of any use. I then dedicated myself to trying to learn to pace accurately, and soon managed a pace that fitted nicely when used on the base map with the 1:2500 scale of the triangular rule. This "Bates pace" was a purely arbitrary unit, but it worked well enough for our purpose. I learned to make nice adjustments in scrambling over coral boulders and around breadfruit trees and through fern thickets so that I could come out with the proper count. In crossing the island, plotting the course on the outline map made from the air photos, we generally found an error of five or ten feet (it was about 900 feet across Falarik). This would probably have been disgraceful for an engineer but it pleased us immensely.

First we tried noting compass directions and number of paces for the quirks in the paths with the idea of plotting these on the map later. But this didn't work—too many mistakes. So I tried making a plane table by sinking a German camera adapter-screw into a board so that it could be fastened to an American camera tripod. The resulting contraption could not be called sturdy, but I was very proud of the improvisation.

We quickly worked out an effective system for dealing with trails. The mapping team consisted of Don, Bakal, Tony and me. Don handled the plane table, equipped with the triangular rule, the compass and a towel for switching away flies. Bakal toted things. Tony scouted ahead on the winding trails. I would keep an eye on Tony and when he seemed about to disappear on a trail, would call out to him to wait and then pace directly toward him. Don would sight on Tony (or me on arrival) to get the direction, and I would call back the paces so that Don could draw directly on the base map.

The main trail of Falarik, which I got in the habit of calling "the broad highway," or sometimes "el camino real," ran through the coconut grove parallel to the lagoon shore, generally twenty or thirty yards in from the water. It was about two yards wide, and neatly marked on each side by a row of moss-covered coral rocks. This broad highway ran between the Fan Nap and the lagoon, and passed directly in front of five of the big canoe houses that faced the lagoon along the Falarik shore. The sixth canoe house on Falarik was away from the trail on the point of land that jutted toward Falalap. There were also two canoe houses on Falalap, one facing the lagoon, and the other facing the pass between the two islands.

The canoe houses, clearly distinguishable on the aerial photographs, were convenient reference points in mapping. They served not only for the storage of canoes, nets, lines and other gear, but also as social centers for the men of the atoll. Groups gathered there to talk, or rest, or weave nets, or carry on the never-ending job of making twine or rope from sennit, coconut fiber. A big sea-going canoe was being built in the Falepenach canoe house, near the Fan Nap, during the summer of 1953. This provided me with a convenient and continuing subject for photography.

The broad highway ran for almost a mile along the lagoon shore of Falarik, extending considerably beyond the last habitation, toward the north end of the island, ending abruptly in the middle of nowhere. This northern tip of the island, beyond the end of the trail, was a wild tangle of vegetation, relatively little visited and little used. Except for this northwest tip, the whole of the lagoon margin of the island was a park-like coconut grove, kept clear of weeds or shrubs with almost no other kind of tree—only an occasional breadfruit tree near the household areas, and a few other things like the big *Barringtonia* by the Sabolap canoe house.

The entire course of the broad highway was thus through the open coconut grove. The habitations were mostly set at some distance back from the highway, near the "boondock line."

We picked up that word "boondock" in Guam, and very useful it proved to be. It became an important part of the Abbott-Bates vocabulary, and may well have also infected the Ifalukian speech. In Guam, it was used to refer to the wild tangle of miscellaneous vegetation that had taken over so much of the island after the disruption of the war.

The boondocks on Ifaluk were the parts of the atoll that were not clearly something else—that is, not coconut grove, not taro swamp, not household area. The boondocks were not exactly wild, because all sorts of useful things grew there, including planted coconuts and breadfruit trees. They were not exactly cultivated either. Such areas could thus hardly be called "jungle" or "scrub"; and "forest" seemed rather inappropriate. "Boondock" was just the word; though we could perhaps better have used the Ifalukian equivalent, niwel.

The boundary between the coconut grove and the boondocks was sharply defined: weeds and shrubs were kept cleared out of the coconuts only up to this definite line—the boondock line. This again roughly paralleled the lagoon shore, fifty or sixty yards in. We plotted it on our map, later, when the trail mapping seemed fairly well in hand.

The habitations, deep in the coconut grove and near the boondock line, were grouped into "households." The census showed that there were twenty-six such households on the atoll, eleven on the island of Falalap, and fifteen on Falarik. The Falarik households were not scattered evenly along the highway and lagoon, but formed two clusters or villages, one called Rauau, at the south end of the island—the Fan Nap was in the middle of this—and the other called "Falarik" (the address would probably be "Falarik, Falarik") with a gap of about a quarter of a mile along the broad highway between the two.

The whole system of land ownership of the island was built around these households, each of which had a name. Later in the summer we tried to map the holdings of one household, Falepenach. These holdings included not only the immediate vicinity of the living quarters, but also several patches of boondock and coconut grove on Falarik, and patches in the big taro swamp on Falalap. The patch arrangement seemed to provide that each household would "own" its share of each of the different kinds of land.

The households varied greatly in size, from one which included only one old man and one old woman, to another (Falepenach) which had twenty-six persons. The household system was matrilineal, and when a man married he moved into the household to which his wife belonged. In the matter of what belonged to which household, a man generally seemed to know much more about the household of his mother than about the household of his wife, even though he had been living in the latter for many years. There was considerable informal movement among the households—people sometimes eating and sleeping regularly in a household to which they didn't really "belong"— which introduced a considerable element of confusion into the census making. This informality plus clan relationships and other family ties meant that labor was not strictly apportioned by household—the two old people who officially represented the smallest household were as well looked after as old people would be in a household with numerous members. Everyone really "belonged" to the whole island.

This matter of "belonging" had been on my mind ever since reading that thought-provoking short novel by Carson McCullers, *Member of the Wedding*. The "security" of the children of Ifaluk impressed us from the very beginning. Every child was a member not only of a family and a household, but of the whole island society. A child crying would be comforted by the nearest adult. Curiously, the children, though "secure", were far from obnoxious—in fact it would be difficult to imagine a more delightful bunch of kids. The "sibling rivalry" that seems to plague every American household was conspicuous by its absence—the mannerly, non-aggressive character of Ifaluk society extended even to the five-year-olds.

The security of the children of Ifaluk is probably still further increased by the widespread system of adoption. Ted found that over a third of the children of the island had been "adopted" by couples who were not their biological parents. When a couple for some reason wish another child, they go to a pregnant woman (who must be of the clan of either the adopting father or adopting mother) and ask if they may adopt the child when it is born. The request, it is said, is never refused. The adopting mother goes to the birth house with the real mother—all children are born in a special house, which is taboo to men—and stays there while the baby is born. The biological mother keeps the baby until it is able to walk, but the adopting mother shares the care and affections from the beginning; and when the baby is able to walk, it moves officially into the household of the adopting parents.

The child thus really acquires an extra set of parents, since it continues all through life to have close association with its real parents as well as with its adopting parents. The child acquires extra sets of "brothers" and "sisters" as well. Don found some difficulty with the word "brother" in teaching English since, while the Ifalukians all knew who were blood brothers and who were not, the matter seemed of little importance to them.

Our friend Yani, for instance, and his wife, Letaweriur, had three children. His oldest had been adopted into his mother's household, Soumat, and his next into his father's household (since his father was a re-married widower with no children by the second wife). Only the youngest had he kept to himself. Yet Yani was with all of his children every day. In this case, Yani and his wife, although they officially belonged in her household, Falepenach, spent most of their time in the Soumat household, since it was less crowded. This sort of casualness gave us a great deal of trouble with that census.

But this is straying from the problem of trying to get the Falarik trails down on the base map. With the broad highway and the canoe houses as fixed points of reference, we started to map the principal trails across the island. Falarik was a crescent, following the curve of the circular atoll reef; it was a little over a mile long, with an average width of about 300 yards. There were a dozen or so trails across the island from the inhabited, lagoon side, to the outer, ocean side.

The first of these, taking off from the canoe house beside the Fan Nap, began as a "highway" rather than a "trail." Like the broad highway, it was a wide, straight path, marked on both sides by lines of moss-covered coral rocks. On the left side of this trail was the dense vegetation of Katelu, the sacred site of the ancient Men's House which was in use in the time of Maur, the island's "culture hero." This sacred spot was never entered by anyone except Maroligar, who was its official custodian. As a result, it was a wild tangle of natural vegetation. At one point on the path by Katelu was a large, fresh-water pool in which Fagolier, the paramount chief, sometimes bathed. On the right side of the trail there was an open grove of high breadfruit trees and other plantings of the Falivelu household.

This trail by Katelu we called the "schoolhouse trail"—because it led directly to the schoolhouse. The schoolhouse was a thatched shed built in a large clearing exactly half way across the island. It had been put up in accordance with instructions, either from the Navy or the Trust Territory, and contained a blackboard and a supply of essential equipment like boxing gloves and basket balls. But how would one go about introducing schooling on Ifaluk? Or should one? The answer to this latter, surely, is "yes" because willy-nilly the Ifalukians must learn to deal with the outer world in these days when that world has become a small neighborhood, and even Ifaluk cannot be protected by its remoteness. But the question of how to introduce this schooling is a complex one for which perhaps no one has a clear answer.

At any rate, the schoolhouse was not used for educational purposes during the period of our stay, but it did have uses. The clearing was a handy place to locate the rain gauge, and the schoolhouse itself, with its open sides, seemed a good place for the regular measurements of shade temperature and humidity. So the area became our meteorological station.

On this south end of Falarik the coconut grove of the lagoon shore extended right around the tip of the island to the ocean side, enveloping the schoolhouse yard. The trail was straight and formal, however, only as far as the school; beyond it became a winding footpath leading through the coconuts to the ocean beach.

Except for this southern end and the long stretch of lagoon shore, Falarik was covered with boondocks. Coconuts grew all through these boondocks, and the principal forest tree was breadfruit. But there were a dozen other kinds of trees, and a thick underbrush of bushes and ferns—ferns everywhere. There were many swampy areas in the center of the island, but the land became slightly higher toward the ocean shore, the surface rough with coral boulders, culminating in a definite "boulder ridge" paralleling the ocean beach.

The beach on the ocean side was narrow, sloping rather steeply from this boulder ridge. Along most of the length of the island the beach, too, was covered with coral rocks, but there were also stretches of coral sand. Out from the beach there was a hundred yards or so of coral platform, largely exposed at low tide, then finally the edge of the reef itself against which the great rollers of the Pacific broke their force all the year around.

The other inhabited island, Falalap, was rather different: a large, rounded blob sticking out into the sea and spoiling the neat circle of the atoll. The habitations were all on the northwest end of the island, across the narrow pass from Falarik. Here, too, there was a maintained park-like area, corresponding to the lagoon-side coconut grove of Falarik: but on Falalap, coconuts and large breadfruit trees were interspersed, giving a different "feel" to the landscape.

The center of Falalap was largely a great swampy area carefully cultivated by the women of both islands. Two kinds of aroids (taro), *Colocasia* and *Cyrtosperma,* were grown there for their edible, starchy roots which, with breadfruit, formed the staple food of the atoll. We did not get around to exploring this region in any detail until late in the summer.

The mapping operation was kept up fairly steadily for several days, but there were always intermissions. On Friday afternoon—the second day of the mapping—Bakal and Yani had no difficulty in persuading us to knock off mapping and go spear fishing. We all piled into Bronson's skiff and rowed over to the shore of Ella, outside the pass into the lagoon. Don was rather snooty about this skiff, remarking that a Western rowboat looked like a garbage scow beside the trim and speedy Ifalukian canoes. But Yani and Bakal liked it—perhaps partly because it was foreign, but also because it was steady and because it could hold several people easily. Don, maintaining his scorn, called it the BWUP after one of the more ungainly species of trigger-fish.

Yani and Bakal each had steel-pointed wooden spears, about fifteen feet long; and short, slender steel spears. The long spears were for poking; the short spears were shot from a sling. The sling looked like a strip of inner-tube; at one end was a string loop, tied on firmly; at the other end the rubber was tied into a loop just large enough to slip over the thumb. With the rubber loop over the right thumb, the string loop was pressed over a slight notch in the butt of the spear, and the spear then simply pulled back with the left hand and let go. It worked like a

Hawaiian sling spear, with the hand replacing the hollow bamboo grip.

Fish were not too plentiful and all were small. In a short time Bakal got four small surgeon fish of two species and a small bright-colored reef fish. None were over five inches long—which showed that small fish were not scorned as food.

Don had taken his Arbalete spear gun—a complicated and lethal weapon that had as yet hardly been tried. Yani borrowed it, and Don was greatly cheered to see him miss a couple of shots—Don had been feeling sheepish about his own misses. Presently there were loud shouts from Bakal and Yani. Yani, for fun, had shot a big moray eel with the Arbalete gun. (For fun because the Ifalukians do not eat moray eels. Ted explained this as a sort of pact: the Ifalukians did not eat morays or sharks, with the idea that the morays and sharks would reciprocate. The pact was occasionally violated by both the morays and the sharks.)

The spear was deep in the neck of the big eel, but the eel was still lively enough so that we did not dare try to bring it into the boat, and it was impossible to get it off the spear. So we rowed all the way home towing the speared moray behind the boat. After dragging the eel up on the beach, we managed to get the spear out. Don, Bakal and Yani then started out again, swimming, to try for more fish among the coral heads of the lagoon in front of the Fan Nap.

Don got a fine chance at a blue crevelley about a foot long, and hit him right through the middle. Just then, Yani swam up and pointed to a big moray eel completely out of the rocks and swimming rather feebly along the sandy bottom twelve feet below. The eel was partly on its side and seemed to be looking up at them. The thought flashed through Don's mind that some fool had thrown the speared moray back into the lagoon, and there it was, out for revenge.

They had just started to get themselves out of there when a big shark shot by—a huge, grey torpedo. It made a swift circle around Don, Yani and the eel. Yani shouted and thrashed the water with his hands and feet, at the same time making for the nearest coral head, yelling for Don to come. Don was close behind, still with the speared fish. They clambered onto the platform of coral, where they were standing in water about halfway up their thighs, Don holding the fish and spear high out of the water, trying to avoid attracting the shark with blood. Once more the shark swept by, this time with a second shark just behind. Bakal swam out to the reef, in response to Yani's yells, carrying one of the big, long spears, while Toroman rowed out with the BWUP to pick them all up.

Yani had fished around the coral heads of the lagoon all of his life, and said he had never before seen sharks come in so close to shore. He had a theory that the noise of the spear gun had attracted them. It seemed more likely to Don that they had followed the nice trail of blood from the speared moray, dragged all of the way across the lagoon from outside the pass (where sharks were common) to the area off the Fan Nap. The speared moray was still lying on the coral sand, so the one they had seen behaving so queerly in the lagoon was another.

The day ended with a fine fish dinner.

Ted turned on the radio that evening to listen to some music and presently accumulated an audience of several Ifalukians who had happened to drift by. The next evening people started accumulating on the temple grass behind the Fan Nap shortly after dinner, and it soon became apparent that they wanted another radio concert. The news, apparently, had spread that this was possible. We were a little appalled at the prospect of having to give a radio concert every evening, none of us being much addicted to radios. We explained that the battery would get tired if it were worked too hard. Then Don happened to think of the phonograph.

The expedition had been equipped with a portable, wind-up phonograph. No one knew whose idea this was—perhaps a hang-over from some previous atoll expedition with a juke-box addict among its members. The accompanying records mostly looked like juke-box material, though of uncertain vintage, along with a few records of Hawaiian music.

We pulled down the box of records, which had been stored away high on a beam in the Fan Nap, and set up the phonograph on the temple grass lawn back of the camp. Tony, eagerly helping, said he knew all about phonographs—that experience with the Coast Guard Station on Ulithi again—so we turned the machine and records over to him. This arrangement worked well, and soon the concert was in full swing. I watched for a while from the side lines, caught by the contrast of the brown, naked bodies sprawled on the smooth lawn, listening to jazz records on a portable phonograph.

Presently another aspect of the contrast was brought to our attention —which served also as an illumination of the pocket problem. Nudity, or the seminudity of a loin-cloth, has one great drawback—there are no pockets. Of course, pockets don't necessarily follow from clothing, as any woman in the modern West well knows. But the absence of clothing does necessarily result in an absence of pockets. The men of Ifaluk and the women of the West, for their different reasons, thus share the problem of how to carry small useful objects of the sort that the Western male so conveniently stuffs in his pockets. The solution, in both cases, has been the purse. The men of Ifaluk always carried their purses with them—capacious, neatly woven affairs, which they put beside them when they sat down and tucked under their arms as they walked. What, we often wondered, were the contents of such a purse?

We got some insight, on this occasion, from Tony. After three or four records, he remarked to me that he thought the needle should be changed. I remembered we had come across needles in our unpacking, but for the life of me I couldn't remember where we had put them.

"Oh, that's all right," said Tony.

And he started to fish around in the depths of his purse. Presently he emerged with a small package and started to peel off the layers of wrappings of dried banana leaf, to disclose, finally, a paper of phonograph needles.

The answer to our question about the contents of the Ifalukian purse was clear—it might contain anything. Which I suppose would also be the answer in the case of the female purse of the West. Only Tony, carting his precious packet of needles from Ulithi to phonographless Ifaluk, seemed to have attained a state of preparedness hardly equalled by the White Knight. And yet, as Tony so triumphantly demonstrated, you never can tell!

I was, then, in no way surprised, a few days later, to have Tony pull a small tube of yellow oxide of mercury out of that same purse, and ask me what it was for. When I explained, he graciously gave the tube to Tom, who had granulated eye-lids.

On Sunday (it was the 5th of July by then) I was just contemplating a siesta after a hard morning of mapping, when the peace of the island was broken by cries of "sail-ho" picked up and relayed from the windward side of Falalap across to Falarik in no time at all. Bakal arrived almost as fast as the cries, all out of breath, with Tony soon after, to report that it was a big Navy ship with the number "59" on the prow. The busy crossroads again.

We got out the walkie-talkies, but all we could hear was the "testing," "testing" of one another. The ship wasn't talking. Maroligar dragged a brand new American flag out of the chest by the Fan Nap altar, passing over two tattered ones that had been lying on top, and with Don's help tried to get it on the flagpole, which had been considerably damaged by the typhoon. They finally achieved a sort of half-mast effect—to the considerable puzzlement of the ship's captain, it turned out later.

Ted decided not to let anything as routine as a Navy visit to Ifaluk interfere with his siesta. Don and I, less blasé, haunted the beach until the grey hulk of a destroyer emerged from behind Falalap to anchor off the pass. A small boat put off immediately. When it beached, it turned out to have several cases of equipment identifiable as belonging to Bob Rofen. The crew said there was more cargo aboard. Don hardly dared believe that this might include his missing equipment. He and I went back to the ship with the boat and there, sure enough, were Don's drums, so carefully and lovingly packed in Pacific Grove months before.

We went into the wardroom and had coffee with the officers and told them all about Ifaluk. We borrowed paper, envelopes and stamps to surprise our wives with letters. When Ted came aboard, bringing money, we bought as many cartons of cigarettes as we could at the ship's stores, but this was the only thing we could think of that might be useful. The Ifalukian consumption of cigarettes was enormous— every adult on the island had the nicotine habit—and we were the only source of supply, since no trade ship had visited the island for some months.

The captain went ashore on the final trip of the ship's launch. Most of the local population was assembled on the temple grass by the Fan Nap, all decked out with garlands in the hair and wreaths over the shoulders. I introduced the captain to Fagolier. It was a pleasure to watch the chief on such an occasion. He didn't need clothing for dignity: composed and calm, he always seemed pleased to meet the visitors, murmuring the correct phrases in Ifalukian, with no hint of the naked savage meeting civilization. Rather, the overdressed foreigners seemed awkward and out of place.

The captain photographed everyone, called in the sailors who had been wandering around, and took off. We all went down to the beach to see them go, but unhaunted by any desire to be going along. Don, of course, was terribly pleased to get his missing equipment: and I should have been pleased too, since I came to depend on that equipment for the rest of the summer.

That evening there was dancing. Ted thought at first that it was the children, but it turned out to be the young men, lined up by a bonfire, practicing for some big event that they planned presently. I popped flashbulbs at the dancers and Don and Ted watched, while the mosquitoes drained their blood away—another flaw in paradise. The scene was wild and lovely, the dark backdrop of the coconut palms fitfully lit up by the fire, the row of naked bodies trimmed with flowers and anklets and bracelets of coconut leaves, the inflected chanting, the stomping, clapping and rhythmic movement. Don learned pretty well to get the nice resonance that they produced by clapping the cupped right hand against the inside of the bent left arm.

Don got sore at me for popping flashbulbs—he said it spoiled the atmosphere, was an insult to the Ifalukians, and so forth. I suppose I felt sheepish about intruding with a camera myself—but I had thought I was doing my duty in getting a photographic record. Anyway, I took off with my camera in a huff and kept a residuum of photographic inhibition all of the rest of the summer. The camera is a curious thing that way—it takes gall or cheek or impertinence to get good pictures

and the photographer is apt to be much resented. Yet people like to
see the pictures. I never could see that the Ifalukians minded my photographic habits. They tended at first to stop work and pose when they
saw me with the camera, but they quickly got the idea that I wanted
them to continue working without paying any attention to me. The
kids were particularly cooperative since (it was Ted's idea) I always
had a pocket full of hard candies for distribution.

The people from Satawal left the next morning, Monday. I forgot
to mention that when we arrived on Ifaluk, we found we had been
preceded, a few days earlier, by a set of visitors from Satawal, another
atoll about 150 miles to the east: three of the big ocean-going canoes,
carrying thirty-seven men and boys, two women, two young girls and
two babies. They were making a round of visits to the islands of the
area in the traditional style, and during their stay on Ifaluk they were
guests of the community.

Here in the Western Carolines the knowledge and practice of navigation with ocean-going canoes persists, while it is only a dim memory in
most parts of the Pacific. Here too it will surely and perhaps promptly
disappear, since it is, by any reckoning, a hazardous affair. The palus,
the captain-navigators, of Ifaluk were all old men, and few of the
young men seemed to be learning the art. The young men that we
questioned had all travelled rather widely among neighboring atolls—
but mostly in trade ships, or in the course of being moved about for
labor by the Japanese during the war. Yani, for instance, who had
travelled a great deal in ships, going to Yap to work on the airstrip,
and to Palau for the start of his teacher education, had made only two
canoe trips—both to nearby atolls—and he had no interest in further
canoe travel.

The navigating methods of the Polynesians and Micronesians are
not too well understood, and no European has ever accompanied them
on an ocean voyage—or at least no European has ever written an
account of such a voyage. Ted, in consequence, wanted very much to
go with the Satawal flotilla which was heading next for Elato, some
fifty miles to the east. Ted pointed out that while the trip might be
hazardous, it was surely no more hazardous than driving on a parkway
in the United States on Sunday, which millions of people did with no

qualms. He asked Tom if he could not arrange a crew to take his wa
terach, sea-going canoe, and go along. Tom said he could, but that he
would have to get permission from the chiefs.

When the decision was made to sail that Monday morning, Ted had
high hopes that he could go along. He made it seem very simple. I
didn't know whether to volunteer to go along or not; I don't know
whether he would have taken me anyway, but I was scared at the
prospect of having to make some decision. But the decision was taken
away from us.

We heard Maroligar blowing on his conch shell down by the beach,
to call the chiefs together. Shortly after, the three navigators from
Satawal came to pay us a farewell call, along with Fagolier, Maroligar
and Tom. Tom announced to Ted the chiefly decision:

"Those chief 'e say 'no'. Suppose too much wind. Suppose typhoon
'e come. That canoe 'e go roll, roll, roll. Bimeby fall down in salt
water. You *die*.

"Suppose you want go 'nother island, 'e got steamer. 'E got that
Navy boat. You take 'im."

I felt a great sense of relief. Ted took it nobly, though surely his
last chance for this great anthropological scoop was going with those
canoes. He couldn't question the chiefly decision: but he could at
least use the incident to show that chiefly government on Ifaluk was
operating, and that the chiefs felt secure enough to deny a request
backed by the enormous prestige of an anthropologist representing the
occupying American power.

Ted decided he would at least get as thorough a description of the
embarkation as he could. He put a case of corned beef in the rowboat
and we set out for Falalap, Bakal and a friend at the oars and Don and
me armed to the teeth with cameras. We got there just in time to see
the last of the three big canoes rolled down into the water, and to
follow the provisioning and stowing of the baggage—mostly big
wooden chests that looked as though they might be of Japanese manu-
facture. Finally the passengers started to embark. The few women and
children among these crawled into little thatched huts built out over
the water on each canoe, on the opposite side from the outriggers. It
certainly looked like cramped quarters.

Ted dealt out his forty-eight cans of beef as a going-away present. The chief palu acknowledged this with a short but elegant-sounding speech.

We rowed out to the pass to watch the canoes put up sail when they had passed out of the lagoon—a pretty sight. Three sturdy canoes starting out confidently across the Pacific to hit another tiny atoll—perhaps no staggering distance away, but still something to find without instruments.

CHAPTER IV

FISHING—AND BAKALIZING

TUESDAY morning was started by one of the chiefs blowing a series of resonant blasts, down by the lagoon shore, on a horn made from a large Triton shell. This was the signal for a general assembly. The chiefs had decided that the island needed cleaning up, and word had gone round that the start should be made today. The ground of the coconut grove along the lagoon had been littered with trash ever since the storm, particularly noticeable on the fine lawn of Japanese temple grass around the Fan Nap.

The cleaning was unhurried. The ground was swept with short brooms made from coconut leaves or from old coconut flower stalks with the branches held together by a binding of sennit cord. Much of the sweeping was done from a comfortable sitting or squatting position and the trash was gathered into neat piles to be burned later. The clean-up started at the south end of the island, the people gradually working north. At noon, when about half of the Rauau area was finished, Maroligar again sounded the trumpet and everyone knocked off for the day.

Don and I spent the morning trying to get things more organized around camp. There were Don's drums to be unpacked. He now had a typewriter and a small but very useful reference library and all sorts of goodies like specimen jars, thermometers, hydrometers for measuring salinity, and extra trousers which had been used for packing material. I promptly scrounged a pair of trousers. I had come to the island with two pairs of blue jeans and some T-shirts by way of clothes, and first off had cut the legs of both pairs of blue jeans to convert them into shorts. The trouble was that my legs kept getting scratched in the course of pacing through the underbrush. Then the cuts would get nasty infections. I was ready to abandon my principles and take to long trousers, at least for work in the boondocks.

These infections were another of the flaws in paradise. Staphylococcus would start growing happily in every little skin abrasion, turning it into a nasty sore. The infections yielded fairly readily to antibiotic ointments, but this involved daily sessions of "wound-licking" and an ever-present decoration of band-aids over the scratched skin surfaces. This bothered me particularly because it was a contradiction of my pet theories about the intrinsic healthfulness of the tropical climate.

The whole question of "tropical sores" is a puzzling one. Coral cuts are notoriously troublesome, but on Ifaluk it seemed to make no difference whether the cut was made by coral or by the saw-like margins of the pandanus leaves. It might have been special susceptibility by newcomers to local bacterial strains—but the local people often had similar sores. It might have been some nutritional lack—I had seen similar infections in South America clear up quickly with thiamine injections. Certainly, we, with our canned food, were not living on any ideal diet.

Whatever the cause, the sores were a continuing nuisance, and I was very glad to get Don's extra trousers, much as I hated the idea of trousers—an arctic garment not really adapted to a tropical climate.

While Don was stowing his newly arrived gear, I concentrated on trying to set up a drying cabinet for plant specimens, taking one of the big wooden cases and fixing it so that pressed plants could be stored inside over continuously burning kerosene lanterns, to provide a constant, gentle heat. We would need a record of the plants growing on the island, both wild and cultivated, and there was no use starting plant collections without provisions for drying them.

This drying cabinet was put up in the "laboratory tent," a tarp that was suspended between two coconut palms beside the Fan Nap. A big mosquito net was hung under the tarp and a box to serve as table put inside. We frequently worked there during the day, to get away from the flies, and during the evening, to get away from the mosquitoes. Ted stuck to the Fan Nap for writing up his notes—but carefully protected with long trousers tied around the ankles, and with coils of Japanese "punk" burning to exorcise the mosquitoes. He had great faith in that burning punk.

We decided to start the plant collecting that afternoon, since the drying cabinet was ready. It was quite an expedition—Yani, Tony, Bakal, Don and me. The idea was to try to collect not only the plants, but information about them. Tony, as a Ulithi man, didn't know the local plant lore, but he was a good interpreter. Yani's English was rapidly gaining in fluency, however, and he and Don, particularly, were able to understand one another almost from the beginning without outside help. Yani did know the local plants—their names and their uses—and Don would jot down this information while I fussed with the plant press itself. Bakal, as usual, was general handy man.

The clean-up was continued next morning and pretty well finished by noon, when everyone on Falarik gathered on the lawn outside the Fan Nap for a communal meal. "Feast" is probably too strong a word for the meals that invariably followed any community activity. The food was lavish enough, contributed by all of the participating households, but it did not differ markedly from the everyday diet.

In this instance, Ted decided that the occasion was important enough for him to contribute one of the cases of corned beef that he had brought along for just such purposes. The canned beef was a greatly appreciated delicacy, called "carawao," which would seem to stem from the Spanish word for water-buffalo, carabao. Several Ifalukian words reflected Spain's dominance in the Carolines in the 19th century —the word "cat" for instance, which hardly differed from the Spanish gato.

The opened case of beef was put before Maroligar, the number two chief, but the distribution of the cans was carried out by Toroman, the number three chief, who always seemed to take over when there was anything to be divided among the island households. He called out the names of the households, tossing the cans to representatives of each; some cans were set aside for Falalap (which was having its own clean-up), and there was a small, separate pile for the chiefs.

The people had brought many pots of breadfruit, cooked in different ways, and there was a large pile of drinking coconuts—also divided by Toroman. The meal lasted about an hour. I spent most of the time prowling around with the cameras while Ted and Don were more directly participating, squatting with the chiefly group. Ted reported that he liked best breadfruit that had been cooked with coconut cream, resulting in a sort of mashed dough with the white, creamy, semi-sweet sauce.

That evening Don had his regular session of English and Ifaluk language exchange under the gasoline lanterns in the back of the Fan Nap. After the lesson Yani and his friend Tachiwelimeng lingered. They asked about the war between the United States and Japan, and got to telling about their own experiences. Tachiwelimeng had been taken by the Japanese to Fais, where there was a radio station. When the first American ship appeared off the island the Japanese got very excited, radioed the news to Yap, and then disappeared into hiding. The bombardment that followed scared everybody on the island. Tachiwelimeng spoke no English, but he was a born clown and gave a hilariously vivid pantomime of how the noise of the first shell tumbled him, how he crept behind a coconut palm and crouched in a ball, how a shell hit the coconut tree about six feet overhead and blew it down. No one was hurt except one of the Japanese, who was hit in the arm, but not seriously.

Japanese ships later took their captive labor to Yap, to use in filling holes in the landing strip made by the regular American bombings. Tachiwelimeng gave another graphic pantomime of American planes dodging Japanese ack-ack, bombs exploding all over the place and the like. These people seemed to look back on this as a big sideshow, bearing no resentment for the local people killed by the American bombings of Yap, and little resentment against the Japanese for getting them involved there.

The days were beginning to go by with remarkable speed. Ted gravely crossed them off, one by one, on a big calendar posted in the Fan Nap, and there was a check on this in my notebook, where the meteorological observations were entered every morning, first thing after breakfast. All sorts of things went into that notebook (one of those waterproof engineer's books, carried in a case on the belt) and I had a chance to exercise my file-clerk instincts in keeping them straight. Numbers for plant notes had a square pencilled around them, so they caught the eye quickly. Pack and film numbers for photographs taken with the Crown Graphic had a circle around them; numbers for the Leica were double underlined; numbers for the Kodak Reflex were distinguished with a triangle.

The only marks for Thursday, July 9th, the day following the clean-up, were triangles, because the only notes were on photographs taken with the reflex. This was because the day was spent on a fishing expedition and I carried only the reflex. I never had liked that camera much, so I carried it whenever I thought there was danger of damage or loss—in this case, danger of salt-water damage.

Most of the men of Falarik were involved in this fishing expedition. Preparations started early in the morning. Great lengths of rope were hauled out of the canoe houses and wound spirally with strips of palm leaves, one after another, until the effect was that of a huge pile of monstrous green tinsel. The lengths of rope, as soon as they were prepared, were carried down to the lagoon shore and piled into the canoes.

By about ten o'clock everything was ready and the flotilla of canoes pushed off—a couple of dozen of them, the small one-man kind, and the medium-sized kind that carried four or five men. None of the big, sea-voyaging canoes were launched. We went, with Bakal and Yani, in Bronson's rowboat, the BWUP, named for the ungainly trigger-fish. We felt awkward and sedate in this tub, but we were afraid of being a nuisance if we asked to go in one of the canoes. Anyway, Yani and Bakal were enamored of the BWUP, and it did make a steady base for observation and photography.

There was a row of about a mile across the still, bright lagoon. We took turns at rowing as a matter of principle, of sharing activities. But I am no athlete under any circumstances, and I was perhaps too obviously glad when I could stop the rowing and stretch out on the prow of the boat with head overside, staring into the mysterious sapphire depths. The lagoon deepened rapidly, but there were areas, even in the center, where it was only thirty or forty feet deep, and the shadows of coral heads below could be made out.

Presently the water began to shoal again, as we approached the reef. For a while the boat could be maneuvered through the sandy channels among the coral heads but all hands had to walk across the reef itself while the boat was pulled through a narrow, shoal, "canoe pass" which, although only a few inches deep, was clear enough of coral to enable the canoes to be floated across the reef.

I was wearing alpargates, South American canvas sandals, excellent for rain forest, but no good for coal reefs—this was the last day in the life of those sandals, and I had to use great care to make them last even for the walk across the reef. Yani and Bakal were managing nicely in their bare feet, which showed the incredible toughness that the human hide can reach, but even they were walking carefully.

It was something over a thousand feet across the reef. On the far side, on this still morning, there was only a gentle surf from waves averaging only a foot or so high. This was the lee side of the atoll, in terms of the trade winds, but at this season when the trades were not blowing and when the rain was often from the west, the breakers here could be very high, a pulsating line of white on the horizon from the view point of the Fan Nap.

The BWUP was pushed out beyond the breakers and boarded again. Here, outside the reef, was the shark zone, but none were seen all day. Yani said one of his relatives had been attacked by a shark in this region, but had saved himself by pulling off his loin-cloth and covering the eyes of the shark as he charged by.

The reef shelved off gradually and details of the bottom could be made out clearly in twenty-five or thirty feet of water. The bottom was solidly encrusted with life—corals, coralline algae, sponges and the like—except for the narrow, smooth "surge channels," kept clear by the rush of water along the bottom returning from the surf. They were like ravines along a mountain front.

The canoes started playing out the coconut-bedecked rope, finally forming a huge semicircle out from the reef. The rope was weighed down with coral-block anchors and attached to each of the regularly-spaced canoes with a line. A large V-shaped seine was set in the middle of the semicircle, its bottom and sides over one of the ravines. When all was ready, groups of men on the reef at each end of the semi-circle started hauling in on the rope, bringing the two ends continually closer together, so that eventually a big circle was formed with the off-shore edge just in back of the apex of the seine.

Everyone was in the water except the men hauling on the ends of the rope, the canoes being pulled along as the circle contracted. Every-one who owned them wore goggles, and with goggles the whole theory of the operation was clear. The frightening line of weaving fronds moved slowly along the bottom, driving hordes of fish of all colors, shapes and sizes before it. The swimmers followed along with the rope, and as the circle got smaller and smaller and the water more and more shallow, the circle of swimming men formed an additional barrier above the palm fronds. The fish, milling frantically inside the barrier, were finally driven into the seine, which was then closed, pulled up between two canoes, and the contents ladled into another canoe with a dip net. When the seine was up, many of the men went in with spears and dug out the fish hiding among the coral boulders.

This process was repeated three times during the day, the canoes and seine being moved each time to a new position along the reef. The total catch for the day was one of the middle-sized canoes about half full of fish. This was not regarded as a really good catch, but every-one seemed reasonably happy, and the fishing expedition, accompanied by a great deal of laughter and horseplay, was a fine combination of business and pleasure.

The BWUP with its passengers was sent in over the reef ahead of the rest, since it was so slow. The whole flotilla had moved around the reef toward the north end of Falarik during the course of the day, and the BWUP, on the way home, pulled in to this part of the island, where Yani and Bakal scouted for drinking coconuts. We all sat, re-laxed, on the trunk of a fallen coconut for our drinks, and for the first cigarettes of the day. Because smoking before or during a fishing ex-pedition is taboo.

The canoes came dashing home across the lagoon in fine style and by the time we got to the Fan Nap the canoe-load of fish had been pulled out and dumped, ready for distribution. This, as always, was the special function of Toroman. Five big red fish were put in a pile by themselves, for the chiefs, and there was another pile of special kinds of fish, mostly trigger-fish, set aside by custom for the old men. The remainder of the catch was sorted out roughly by size into piles of large, medium-sized and small fish. In the meanwhile, men representing each of the various households gathered around, smoking and chatting. All had freshly-woven coconut baskets for their share of the catch. These baskets, quickly made from the green palm frond, were the ordinary packaging material of the island.

In the first round, Toroman tossed to each man two of the larger and three of the middle-sized fish. Then each got ten to twenty fish from the middle-sized and small piles, the number depending on the size of the fish and the number of people in the household. Then every family got one more large fish.

Don and Yani weighed a few specimens of the different kinds and sizes of fish, and calculated that the total catch was about 630 pounds. About forty pounds of the smallest fish were thrown out as too small for use, or because they were of kinds considered inedible. The seine catch as distributed, amounted to about two pounds of fish per individual inhabitant.

Everyone had fish that evening, and very good it was. Several of the most prized kinds of fish were given to us. These were expertly fileted by Bakal, and equally expertly fried by Ted in bacon grease after being rolled in corn meal. Ted was a master at this. Jobs around the Fan Nap were generally pretty equally shared, but Don and I always tried to maneuver Ted into the fish frying job—not, for once, out of indolence, but because he really did have a touch. The Ifalukians generally roasted fresh fish like these whole over coals from small coconut-husk fires, and they were awfully good that way, too.

This kind of fishing, with giant rope-and-coconut-leaf tinsel dragged over the coral bottom of the outer reef, was called rop fishing. Whether Ifalukian rop had any connection with English rope was questionable. Ted thought the similarity coincidence, since the rop fishing must have been an ancient practice, long antedating any contact with English.

The Ifalukians, like the people of all of the old Micronesian and

Polynesian cultures, had almost endless ways of catching fish. Individuals or small groups fished with spears or with hook and line. A method that appealed to me particularly was to attach the hook and line to a kite, which was sailed from a canoe in the lagoon: thus combining the pleasures of fishing with those of kite-flying (one of the numerous instances where I couldn't decide whether a particular operation should be called "work" or "play"). There were also a variety of ways of trapping fish, with traps ranging from the large, permanent stone weirs built along the lagoon shore, down through various types of wattle traps, to improvised affairs of plaited coconut leaf sometimes set by the women in the shallows—the only fishing operation of the women, aside from collecting crabs, shellfish and the like. Women, in fact, were subject to various sorts of taboos in relation to fishing, and sex was strictly suppressed during a prolonged fishing operation.

There were various ways of catching special fish, like tuna, bonito and flying fish, when these appeared, but I didn't get to see any of these operations. Later in the summer, however, Don and I did spend a very active day trying to get a complete photographic record of a lagoon seining operation—the kind of fishing called yating.

The Ifalukians had an immense supply of seines—great piles stored in each of the canoe houses. The accumulation of seines and of rope seemed a direct consequence of the almost compulsive male habit of making sennit twine. Whenever a group of men were sitting around gossiping, or helping us gather information, or quietly watching the horizon, some of them would pull handfuls of fluffy leached and pounded coconut fibers out of their purses, and start twisting them into twine. This process, like knitting with the women of the West, did not interfere with either conversation or thought; and since it went on constantly, the twine output was considerable. The sennit twine had a great many different uses, but much of it ended woven into seines.

In the case of the particular yating operation that we photographed, the morning started with groups of men shouldering lengths of seine and carrying them down from the canoe houses to load them into canoes beached on the lagoon shore. The canoes took off in orderly procession, each dumping its seine in turn and connecting with the next until there must have been nearly a mile of seine forming a great semicircle out from the shore and back again. Then men on shore started hauling in the seine, moving slowly along the beach to close the circle, a process that lasted from midmorning to midafternoon. Men in canoes were constantly guiding the movement of the seine and as the circle narrowed in shallow water, men with great dip nets stationed themselves along the seine at regular intervals to catch the fish that were frantically leaping out from the milling horde within. Finally, as with rop fishing, the imprisoned fish were driven into traps which were emptied into canoes, to be taken back to the Fan Nap where Toroman, as always, supervised the division of the catch by households.

But the photographing of the yating fishing took place late in the summer. We had only been on the island a couple of weeks when we took part in the rop fishing expedition off the reef and we were full of wonderment about everything that went on about us.

The evening after the rop fishing there was dance practice again. It was going on every evening and I began to develop a theory that daily dancing was a basic element giving cohesiveness to the island's social structure. It seemed to combine the functions of amateur dramatics (participating in activities) and going to the movies (spectator entertainment). In this case the same people were at one time participants and at another time spectators. Even the kids formed their dance groups, clapping and stomping and chanting in shrill, enthusiastic voices—usually in the early evening, before the adult sessions started. (My theory was all right, I think, except that dancing was an intermittent rather than a continuing activity, since there were long danceless periods between the proper ceremonial occasions.)

Even for these practice sessions, the people generally got pretty much dressed up, the men at least wearing garlands of flowers on their heads and coconut-leaf skirts over their loin-cloths. The men of Ifaluk, of course, tended to be the gaudier sex. This may be "natural" not only for man but for animals in general, Western civilization being out of step in this regard. Even in the West it hasn't been so long since the days of bright, embroidered waistcoats, and Hawaiian shirts seem to be spreading now in certain parts of the United States.

At any rate, Ted thought it was time for a present when Bakal

ABOVE There was little clutter on the floor of the houses: most family possessions were slung from the rafters.

BELOW The people of Ifaluk cooperated nicely in the census operation.

LEFT Yaniseman, constant companion and advisor.

RIGHT Totogoeiti (Tom), navigator and interpreter.

BELOW Fagolier, the paramount chief; and Gavileisei, craftsman and canoe builder.

RIGHT Sagolimar, who often worked with us.

LEFT Gauaisig, navigator and canoe builder.

BELOW Toroman, the number three chief and official divider of food.

ABOVE The boondocks were not exactly wild; they were not exactly cultivated either.

BELOW We tried to collect botanical specimens of all of the kinds of plants on the atoll.

turned up at the Fan Nap ready for dancing after the day of fishing, with a garland of flowers in his hair, big lilies in the holes in his ear lobes, and a fresh green coconut skirt over his red loin-cloth. Ted had noticed the Ifalukian passion for ornament when he was there before, and this time came prepared with appropriate gifts, especially a good supply of ropes of the tinsel used for decorating Christmas trees. He got out a length of this tinsel for Bakal, who was delighted. Bakal ran his big, wooden comb through his hair several times to make it stand out stiffly (it stuck up in a great puff about three inches high anyway) and wound the tinsel around it in a double strand from the top of his head, at a rakish angle that brought it low over the right ear. A very flashy get-up for a young blade.

After two weeks on the island, we had become somewhat relaxed in this matter of male ornamentation. The people from the first would offer us maramars—garlands of flowers—for our hair, and we would accept them politely and appreciatively—and wear them sheepishly. But the sheepishness wore off rapidly. Presently I found myself expressing admiration for the effect of a wreath of velvety yellow four-o'-clocks on Don, and Don would notice the nice touch of bright red hibiscus on my black hair. Ted's beard was approaching magnificence, even at this early stage and made a fine accompaniment for flower garlands. After a while we reached the point of nailing up a mirror in the Fan Nap, so that we could arrange our garlands tastefully and appropriately before sallying forth in the morning. This process came to be known as "bakalizing" after one of its most devoted practitioners.

It was interesting to watch the process of disintegration of Western male prejudices in ourselves. The necklace given me by Tachi was one step in this process. Tachi, a boy perhaps twelve years old who lived near us, cut his foot very badly one day on a coconut shell. He came to me for help and I dressed the foot regularly every morning until the wounds had healed. Tachi, in gratitude for this doctoring, brought me a beautiful cowrie-shell necklace.

I put on the necklace doubtfully, expecting jeers from Ted and Don. But instead they both, with obvious envy, said how nice it looked! I wore it for a day and generously offered to lend it to Ted and then to Don. The loan was accepted, and for a long time I could only wear

my necklace every third day, when it came my turn. Presently they
were given necklaces, too, and then we could all be properly orna-
mented all the time!

Don kept on with the regular English lessons. He wrote a journal
entry about one evening when Yani had brought a simple English
reader from the school supplies and wanted to know the meanings of
some of the words—believe, would, parade, party (that was easy),
Halloween, conversation, as, think, exactly. Don felt he did nicely—all
his teaching instincts came to the fore. He consulted me once or twice,
but this obviously would lead only to an argument that would leave
the English lesson suspended indefinitely—"exactly" was perfect for
an Abbott-Bates argument. Its meaning could hardly be touched on
without previous exploration of the nature of reality and the percep-
tions of the observer, and once this was started, "exactly" could never
be reached again. So Yani got only the Abbott interpretations of meaning.

There seemed to be little trouble about the explanations, and this set
Don to thinking about the nature of "savages." According to Ted, these
people of Ifaluk had had the least contact with the West of any of the
Pacific islanders—only the people of central New Guinea being comparable. Thus, by common Western standards, they would be classed
as "savages"—in fact, as "naked savages." Yet, Don argued, these are
really highly sophisticated people, so startlingly like Westerners that
it was sometimes hard to remember that there were any differences
at all. He was particularly impressed by their sense of humor, which
seemed to differ not at all from his own. They laughed at his jokes
when they understood them, as he did at theirs. Humor that didn't
cross the cultural barrier seemed to be associated either with the
double meanings of language, or with cultural traits that were not
shared. Don wrote these impressions in his journal—from which I am
cribbing.

After the English session, we all went to watch dancing on Falalap.
We took the BWUP and rowed over in the dark, settling down under
the palms near a fire of dry coconut leaves. The women were sitting
in a line, making slow movements of arms, torso and head to the pace
of a slow, low-pitched song that mostly hung on one note, but oc-

casionally rose or dropped over a scale of about three notes. There, in the light of a fire that flared to brightness and sank down almost to darkness as fuel was added or used up, with a row of bare-breasted women singing the pleasant but monotonous dirge-like song, with slow, almost caressingly sensual movements of the hands and arms, Don was overcome again with a feeling of unreality, of the cultural gulf that separated him from them.

But again he thought, this is trivial. The only real barrier is language, and that can be overcome. It was, in fact, already lessening. Just that day, he had been able to explain to a man who brought a wooden bowl to the Fan Nap that Ted was asleep, to tell the man to come back later in the evening, and to ask him whether he wanted tobacco or money for the bowl, and how much. It was a great triumph in communication.

The gulf between California and Ifaluk could be bridged.

CHAPTER V

MOSTLY ABOUT FOOD

MUCH time on Ifaluk was spent in sitting—men sitting around the canoe houses, women sitting around the cook houses. I had the impression that the men were more apt to just sit, and the women to sit and chatter; but this impression was probably a carry-over from preconceived ideas about my own culture. Certainly, in fact, the men in the canoe houses often carried on interminable conversations; but certainly also they were frequently silent and contemplative—or drowsy.

This fitted my temperament fine. Since childhood I have been an inveterate sitter (and day dreamer). My most frequent companion in the sitting process on Ifaluk was Fagolier, the paramount chief. From the beginning he fascinated me with his poise and dignity, his character-lined face. I had a curious feeling of rapport sitting with him, sharing a mat or a coconut log, smoking, occasionally exchanging a grin, but feeling no real need of trying to say anything.

He had all of the qualities that should go with the paramount chieftainship—the assurance and humility of security; a calm, reliable decisiveness; an ever-present courtesy and thoughtfulness. I wondered often what he was really like, how much this picture of him was the product of my own imaginings, whether I saw him as he was, or whether I saw only the projection of my own concepts of a chief. Yet I gained confidence in my mental portrait because it always seemed to correspond with my observations. Then I would still wonder whether this was a tribute to Fagolier, or a tribute to the flexibility of my imagination. But his poise, his dignity, seemed to have a very real quality, completely independent of the trappings of position or pretence.

I remember the evening early in our stay when he stopped by the Fan Nap just as we were starting our dinner of spam, canned sweet potatoes and canned string beans. We asked him to join us, which he did with apparent pleasure, even making noises of appreciation over the string beans—the equivalent in my own household, over new food, of "how interesting." When we were finished he went off with his plate, cup and silver and washed it and started to try to wash a pot! It was like the thoughtful guest back home who insists on helping with the dishes; somehow, as real a gesture of courtesy as I have ever seen.

The next day, when I went to photograph progress on the canoe that was being built in the Falepenach canoe house, I found Fagolier working away with an adze on a plank, the efficient artisan. Usually he was right in the middle of any work in progress, carrying his full load.

He was always the thoughtful host. Everyone on the island was always a thoughtful host—but Fagolier, as chief, along with Maroligar, number two chief and proprietor of the particular spot where the Fan Nap stood, were especially attentive. I noted my impression in my diary one morning when Fagolier brought us fresh coconuts. He came with two handsome boys bearing the nuts, for all the world like two pages attending a prince. The pages placed the coconuts as directed by a wave of the hand, and during the ensuing period of polite silence, they sat quietly and respectfully in the background, so that the feeling of court was maintained.

I watched him directing a dance rehearsal one night. Don was involved with Yani's English and Ted with something else, and when Fagolier and Maroligar left the Fan Nap after their usual check on our comfort, they obviously expected me, at loose ends, to come along with them. When we got to the fire, they seemed to expect me to join the line of dancing men. So—away from the eyes of my fellow Westerners—I did.

Certainly I was very awkward and shortly I abandoned the attempt, but I was glad I tried because it gave me a direct experience with Fagolier as dance director. He squatted by the fire and the line of men formed opposite him against the dark backdrop of the coconut grove. To get some glimmering of what to do, I had to watch both Fagolier and the men in the line beside me, and I gradually got the feel of the situation. The dance involved a series of gestures with both hands, and of vocal sounds that varied from hums to shouts but that did not seem to form word patterns. Fagolier directed this with a remarkable economy of gesture, the indications of his hands being translated into full scale action by the men opposite. He was acting as leader and coordinator—again quietly, skillfully and economically.

These thoughts about Fagolier were precipitated the morning that Don started his food study of the Falepenach household. Don was resolved to be as exact about this as possible. It is very difficult to get precise figures on what people eat under any circumstances (think of the problem of measuring everything scraped off the plate into the garbage can, or of finding out whether Johnny got into the cookie jar this morning, and how many cookies he snitched). But, Don reasoned, the greater effort you made to be precise, the nearer you were likely to come to truth in your measurements. So, with the complete and invaluable assistance of Yani, he started out to measure everything eaten in Yani's household, Falepenach, for a month.

It developed at once that I was about as helpful as a sore thumb in this process. That first morning Don and Yani weighed all of the breadfruit and all of the coconuts brought in for the day's use. Then, to get a measure of the difference between crude and finished product, they waited around while the breadfruit and coconut were being prepared for cooking. Clearly I wasn't needed for either the weighing or waiting processes, so I drifted off to sit down by Fagolier and contemplate the horizon. Don, in the meanwhile, found (among other things) that twenty husked, ripe coconuts, weighing 27 lbs. 5 oz. produced 11 lbs. 13 oz. of copra ready for use in that day's cooking operations in Falepenach.

We had been talking about the problems of the food study from the beginning. A careful study of what people ate, how much, how they got it, how it served them nutritionally, was clearly basic to any attempt at understanding man's relations with the world around him. With the census finished and the mapping well started, food study had next priority.

Each of us had somewhat different ideas about how to approach this difficult job. In the end, records were kept on four different households for a month each. Two of the studies were made by Ted and two by Don. I am not sure, looking back, why I stayed out of this, because food relations have long been one of my pet interests. I think it was chiefly a matter of economy of effort. Ted and Don had the matter well in hand and each had special advantages: Ted because of his familiarity with local customs and with the language, and Don because of his close association with the invaluable Yani. The daily record taking rapidly became routine, and a pattern formed very early by which each of us established his own special daily routines, thereby avoiding duplication of effort. When to collaborate and when to specialize is a nice problem in the team approach to scientific study. I think we handled the division of labor very well, though not always consciously.

Don and Ted have summarized the results of this food study. The details will be published in scientific papers, but perhaps I can give here a general summary.

The four households included a total of forty people, men, women and children: the average weight per person being 95 lbs. The average daily intake of staple food per person per day was: fresh breadfruit, 175 grams; ripe coconut meat, 130 grams; fish, 105 grams; taro, 70 grams; fermented breadfruit, 60 grams; fresh toddy (sap from coconut flower stalks), 415 cc.; milk from green coconuts, 75 cc.; green coconut meat, perhaps 35 grams.

Calculating food values for these materials is not easy, since most detailed nutritional studies have been made with northern foods. The foods of the tropical Pacific, however, have been studied in Hawaii, and there is a growing literature on nutrition in other parts of the Pacific. From this information, it appears that Ifaluk diet is inadequate in several respects, according to the usual dietary norms. The Ifalukians, however, gave every appearance of having an adequate diet—there were no obvious signs of their being undernourished. I have long come to view with suspicion these tables giving comparative nutritional values for different parts of the world. Truly, much of the world suffers from malnutrition as compared with the United States or Western Europe; but also, I think, our nutritionists have failed to give adequate attention to possibly varying needs. The food needs of man in Ifaluk and of man in New York are not necessarily the same.

One problem with diet studies is the difficulty of keeping track of snacks, of occasional foods; yet such occasional or incidental food may be very important in relation to some vitamin or mineral requirement. We were very conscious of this problem, and Ted and Don made every effort to keep track of incidental food as well as of staples. Yani was particularly helpful in this, because he tried to remember and report all of the incidental things that he and his friends ate as they wandered about during the day. On this basis, there was considerable variety in the Ifalukian food. At least thirty kinds of plants were eaten in one way or another (not counting "medicines"). Don got records of eighty-eight different kinds of fish that were eaten, and guesses that there must be many more. For animals, there were also sea turtles, chickens and other birds, and occasionally pigs and dogs. Some seventeen kinds of molluscs were eaten, eight kinds of crustaceans, and a few other things like sea anemones and one kind of sea urchin.

We arrived at the height of the breadfruit season. Breadfruit trees grew everywhere, producing far more fruit than could be used; and the fallen, rotting fruits were probably the chief breeding places of the flies that so plagued us. As the breadfruit harvest dropped later in the summer, so did the numbers of flies.

Breadfruit in its season (June through September, with a second, smaller crop in February and March) is the staple food, the chief source of starch, for the people of Ifaluk. It is a staple on most of the islands of the tropical Pacific—the "bread" of Polynesia and Micronesia.

The big, starchy fruits grow on a handsome tree, probably native to Malaya. It may well be among the most anciently cultivated of plants and the main food varieties are seedless, completely dependent on man for reproduction. It is propagated from shoots which spring up around the base of the trunk, and the colonizers of the Pacific—

Polynesian and Micronesian—had to carry the precious young plants with them on their long canoe voyages to new islands.

The famous expedition of Captain Bligh with the BOUNTY had the purpose of bringing young breadfruit trees from Tahiti for establishment in the West Indies, where the planters thought it would be an ideal food for their African slaves. This first attempt at importing the tree was frustrated by the mutiny, but plants were successfully brought in on a subsequent voyage. Breadfruit, however, never became a staple in the West Indies. People do not adopt new foods easily (not even slaves), and where new staple foods have been adopted—as in the case of the potato in Ireland—it is generally because of overwhelming advantages. Breadfruit seems not to have demonstrated such advantages to any non-Pacific culture.

We went out one morning with Tom and a young man of his household to gather breadfruit. The man who was going to pick the fruit carried a large coil of rope and a long pole which had a short crosspiece firmly tied near one end. We followed him through a complex maze of boondock paths to a large breadfruit tree. He threw the coil of rope over the lowest branch (about twenty feet up) and pulled it out with his pole, so that the rope was hanging double from the branch.

With the aid of the rope he climbed easily up the trunk to this first branch, whence he could scramble to any part of the top of the tree. We watched him walk upright along one horizontal branch about thirty feet above the ground, using his long pole as a sort of balance after the fashion of acrobats. With the pole he was able to break off fruit easily in any part of the tree, allowing the fruit to fall to the ground. The bruising apparently did not matter, though the fruit to be used for food must be gathered before it is completely ripe, while the pulp is still white and mealy.

The fresh fruit is either baked or boiled, with many minor variations in ways of cooking. I didn't think much of it, no matter how cooked. It seemed no better or no worse than potatoes, palatable enough with meat gravy—but the Ifalukians didn't have meat gravy.

Breadfruit is the only food on Ifaluk that can be stored for any length of time (they sometimes smoke fish, but not to keep it for more than a few months). To preserve the breadfruit, the skin is scraped off and the pulp cut into sections which are put into big, open-meshed rope baskets. These are carried to the lagoon, weighed down with coral blocks, and left to soak overnight. The baskets are then removed from the lagoon, covered with leaves, and left for still another night. The pulp can then be kneaded into a paste, which is wrapped in leaves and buried in the ground. The preserving process is quite comparable with that used for sauerkraut, and the stuff lasts for years. We didn't like the taste of this mar, but apparently it is nutritious enough. Considerable quantities are buried every year, insuring a food supply in case of a disaster like a typhoon.

There are seven or eight named varieties of breadfruit, distinguished by the size and appearance of the fruit, shape of the leaves, and the like. In the case of two of the varieties, the fruits have seeds, and in these the roasted seeds are used for food. They have a chestnut-like flavor and quality.

Almost as important as breadfruit were the two taros. This is perhaps doing violence to the word "taro" since it is using it to cover two similar but quite distinct kinds of aroids with edible tubers, one called by the botanists *Colocasia* and the other *Cyrtosperma*. The taro of Polynesia is *Colocasia*, but on Ifaluk both plants were about equally important. These again are anciently cultivated plants, vegetatively propagated, each with endless named varieties. The *Colocasia* on Ifaluk was called wot and the *Cyrtosperma*, pulach (the "ch" is also rendered as an "x" sort of a sound—we argued endlessly about how to spell Ifalukian words).

Both wot and pulach are aroids, that is, they belong to the botanical family that includes the "elephant-ear" plants, the Calla lilies and the Jack-in-the-Pulpit of North America. A third edible aroid, *Alocasia*, called file by the Ifalukians, was grown on the atoll, but it was considered definitely inferior to the other two and little used as food.

Wot and pulach were grown in low, swampy ground in the interior of the islets. The central part of Falalap was almost all swamp, and the main gardens were located there. These taro swamps occur all through the Pacific and it is difficult to know now to what extent they are "natural" and to what extent man-made, because they have been subject to careful cultivation for many generations. The care of the gardens is exclusively women's work and they become expert gardeners. The plants are set in neat rows in rectangular patches, each patch belonging to a particular household so that each household on the atoll has its share of the large Falalap gardens. Weeds grow luxuriously in the rich, mucky soil, and weeding is the main gardening chore. The weeds, I was interested to see, are always buried in the muck, so the practice of "green manuring" is an ancient one here. With young plants, coconut leaves were sometimes used as mulch, to cut down the growth of weeds.

I was greatly impressed, watching these women go about their work, at how little a Westerner would be able to tell them about gardening practices, at how well their methods were adapted to the plants and environment of their atoll. Perhaps one could put this another way, and wonder at how little modern "civilized" man with all his science has been able to improve on, or change, the gardening practices developed by peasant cultures through generations living close to the earth. We have made drastic changes in large-scale agriculture, but the gardener, throughout the world, shares a curiously large fund of common lore.

But I had intended to write here about food, not about agricultural methods. Wot and pulach were eaten to some extent, even during the breadfruit season, just as the preserved breadfruit (mar) was eaten to some extent at other times of the year, making some variation in the daily monotony of starch. There were many slightly different ways of cooking these tubers. We liked best a way of preparing wot (*Colocasia*) whereby it was mashed, cooked with coconut cream, moulded into little balls in a pot, and the whole covered with a thick paste of coconut meat. The effect was a little like that of mashed sweet potatoes served with heavy whipped cream.

Coconut, of course, permeated every aspect of Ifalukian cooking— the milk from green nuts and ripe nuts, the flesh from green nuts and ripe nuts, the sap from the cut flower stalks (here called hachi, perhaps best called "toddy" in English). The coconut was more often used as a supplement in cooking breadfruit or taro, as a seasoning, or the milk or toddy as a liquid for cooking, than as a food in itself. But the green nuts everywhere provided a handy source of drink; and the translucent, jelly-like flesh of these green nuts, eaten after the milk has been drunk, was surely a highly nutritious, though perhaps minor, food.

When a coconut sprouts, the hollow of the nut becomes filled with the white spongy tissue of a special absorbing organ (an extension of the cotyledon). This spongy tissue has a pleasant, sweetish taste and the Ifalukians were very fond of it. It often seemed to me that the juice of green coconuts filled the role on Ifaluk of soft drinks or mid-morning coffee in our culture; and that the spongy tissue of these sprouted nuts corresponded to candy bars, a tasty snack always readily available. The Ifalukian product, in both cases, would seem to be more "healthful" than its Western counterpart.

Toddy, or hachi, the sap that oozed from the cut flower stalks of coconuts, was a very important element in the Ifalukian dietary. Many palms have a strong flow of sap into the large, rapidly-growing flower stalks, and people in several parts of the world have learned to use this—most notoriously in a fermented form. The flow of sap was better in some coconut palms than in others, and on Ifaluk the particularly good palms were marked off for this special purpose of supplying toddy. Every morning and every evening all of the young men of the island were off on their rounds of collection, each with his special beat.

The toddy palms all had notches cut in the trunks to facilitate climbing. A man would go to each of his palms in succession, climb up to the crown, pour the sap accumulated in a coconut shell into the bottle he carried, shear off a thin slice from the end of the cut flower stalk to stimulate sap flow, replace the coconut shell to catch the drip, and go on to the next palm. Several quarts of the fresh sap were thus brought into every household each morning and evening.

The rich, sweetish sap was reserved primarily for the women and children—its place in the diet of Ifaluk seemed to correspond to milk in the diet of the West, and the regularity of the young men with their toddy chores reminded me strongly of the regularity of the milking chore in the rural West. It was, in fact, the only regularity we were able to observe on Ifaluk. Meal hours had no fixed time. There was generally only one large meal in a day, but the time of day at which this was eaten seemed to vary with the whim or convenience of each particular household. The time of toddy-collecting, however, was as unvarying as the sunrise and sunset with which it coincided; and every young man dropped whatever else he was doing at those times to carry out his chore.

Officially, the toddy was always used fresh on Ifaluk. As Ted had found during his first visit to the island, the chiefs had decreed prohibition. They had observed the effect of alcohol on the peoples of some of the neighboring and more Westernized atolls, where the people had easily learned how to distill the fermented toddy into really potent stuff, and they had decided that for the peace and security of the island it would be best if even fermentation were not allowed.

But toddy ferments easily and quickly. We noticed at some of the dance rehearsals an occasional older man with a definitely unsteady gait or a tendency to be too loud or too obvious, and concluded that he had allowed some toddy to follow its natural course by leaving it sit for a day. We had no direct evidence of the violation of prohibition, however, until toward the end of the summer when Tom offered us a sip from his bottle.

The stuff tasted very good to me, though perhaps I am no judge since my taste in alcohol is catholic. It had a pleasant, cider-like tang with, I should judge, about the strength of good beer.

Breadfruit, the two kinds of taro, and coconut, then, were the basic vegetables of the atoll. There were also a number of minor crops—especially papayas and several kinds of bananas and plantains. The papayas were fair, the bananas excellent, but they seemed to be little used by the people. We were often brought cooked green papayas, which have a squash-like texture and taste, and this seemed to be the way they were most commonly used. We were kept constantly supplied with bananas—we always had a bunch or two hanging to ripen in the Fan Nap—but the people seemed to consider them to be children's food. They appeared to prize the banana plants more for the fiber they got from the stem than for the fruit.

Fish formed the basic animal food, but the people also had pigs and chickens. We included domestic animals in our census of the island, and came out with a total of 260 people, five dogs, nineteen cats, thirty-three pigs and fifty chickens. The pig total included animals of all sizes, so pork was not a common article of diet. Only two pigs were slaughtered during the summer, not, as far as we could see, in celebration of any special occasion. The pork was simply boiled instead of being roasted in the traditional Polynesian style.

The fifty chickens were regarded also as a source of occasional meat. We found no instance of the eggs being used for food by the local people. Soon after we set up camp, a young man came around with some eggs which he offered to trade with us for cigarettes. We made a deal and started looking forward to next morning's breakfast. We decided to boil the eggs. It turned out that I liked mine at the three minute stage, the others in a somewhat harder condition. So I dipped my eggs out of the pot at the proper time and started to break one open only to disclose, not the expected runny yolk, but a fully developed chick, ready to hatch! A hasty examination showed all of the eggs to be in the same stage.

I don't know whether this was purposeful or accidental. I wondered whether the people knew of the Phillipine delicacy, balut, and assumed that all outsiders like their eggs in a late stage of development. At any rate, we got the idea across that we would like fresh eggs, and through the summer we were brought a fairly steady supply, always in return for cigarettes. After that first experience, we always carefully candled the eggs, occasionally finding one that seemed to be more chicken than egg, but this apparently by accident.

Although the Ifalukians did not eat chicken eggs, they were very fond of turtle eggs, and these at times turned up in good supply. The albumin of a turtle egg (at least of the eggs of the sea turtles of Ifaluk) does not coagulate on cooking. Don had a strong aversion to uncoagulated egg albumin, and I remember watching his efforts to make a turtle egg in a frying pan turn into something that might look like a respectable egg—yolk surrounded by the conventional white stuff to which we are accustomed. But the turtle egg still looked raw, no matter how long he fried it.

I, of course, made the proper jeers about this culture-bound food aversion of his, which would cut him off from a rich local source of protein. Out of sheer bravado one morning I sucked turtle egg after turtle egg. I got nowhere in my effort to make Don feel foolish (he had great reserves of faith in his own prejudices) but I did make myself very sick. I suspect that the relation between the cramps and the turtle eggs was sheer coincidence; but for the rest of the summer I couldn't face a turtle egg with any more equanimity than Don could, and the eggs that were brought us were disposed of surreptitiously.

The Ifalukians were always bringing us food, more food than we could possibly have eaten with the best will in the world. We protested, but there was no stopping them. Much of it we didn't like— we were a very culture-bound trio, really, perfectly happy with our spam and canned spinach. We felt we couldn't run the risk of hurting the feelings of our hosts by admitting that we didn't much like their breadfruit and boiled pulax, so we would accept the food, eat what we could, and stealthily dispose of the rest in the lagoon at night.

We were always really grateful for gifts of fish, however, and my memories of the summer include the tastiest fish orgies of my whole life. We would turn the fish over to Bakal for fileting and Ted was really a master at rolling the filets in corn meal and frying them in bacon grease as I remarked before, and the Ifalukian fish, fresh out of the transparent waters of the lagoon, were just the right material with which to work.

But while we kept our respect for Ted and the Western method of frying things, we also fell in easily with the Ifalukian method of cooking fish. The commonest and perhaps the tastiest method was simply to roast the fish whole in coals of burned coconut husks. The hardened and carbonized skin could be easily peeled off, to reveal the tasty flesh. I have particularly fond memories of roasted parrot fish. Somewhere, from my Florida childhood, I had got the idea that parrot fish were inedible. I still don't know about the West Indian varieties, but I can certify that the parrot fish of Ifaluk were very edible indeed.

Don and I lost weight during the summer though hardly needing to. I had a gaunt and hungry look, twenty pounds below my normal weight, when I left after three months. I suspect this was our own fault, due to our careless habits of living off casually opened tins of this or that. We might have done better if we had tried to adapt directly to the Ifalukian diet, because certainly the Ifalukians looked healthy and husky enough. Perhaps we couldn't have adapted to their varieties of starch in the time available, since changing food habits involves somewhat more than merely changing prejudices, and changing prejudices is not always easy, particularly when there are three people to interact on one another.

Clearly our own food behavior was not adapted to the atoll conditions, though I am not sure exactly what we did wrong. I always tend to have a skinny, underfed look, in the tropics. It bothers me to have people tell me how well I look after a winter in the north; and how bad I look after a period of tropical residence, because my feelings are exactly the opposite of my appearance. We weighed ourselves periodically on the bathroom scales that we had brought along for weighing the inhabitants of Ifaluk, and I worried a little as I watched the steady drop. But the worry wasn't enough to spoil the pleasure of living in the sun or lazily floating in the lagoon, or enough to jar me into any dietary experiments. We went on opening our cans while we weighed the food at Falepenach and Soumat, dietary intruders but having a wonderful time.

CHAPTER VI

FISH WATCHING

DANCE rehearsals continued almost every night, and it was clear that we were expected to attend despite the interference with both work and sleep. Somehow I didn't understand until some time later that this dance business was largely a response to a request of Ted's. He had particularly wanted, during his first stay on the island, to see some of the important traditional dances, the ur dances, but no such ceremonies had taken place. Before we started for Ifaluk this time, Ted had written to the anthropologist of the Trust Territory Government, expressing the hope that we would be there in the proper season for the dances. The anthropologist had passed the word on to the chiefs by way of the trade ship which called at the island about a month before we arrived.

It turned out that we were too late. The proper time for the ur dances is at the close of the period of ceremonial fishing by torchlight for flying fish. But the Ifalukians, wishing to please Ted, rearranged their ceremonial schedule. They couldn't bring the flying fish out of season, but they could perform the dances.

The dances were really, as Ted explained, a religious ceremonial designed to please the gods. But, as Ted further noted, this did not mean that the content had to take some special religious form: the kindly gods of Ifaluk enjoyed whatever interested the people.

Religion seemed in general very unobtrusive on Ifaluk. There were sacred spots like the altar in the back of the Fan Nap (completely unused during our stay); there was the wild tangle of vegetation in sacred

Katelu where Maur's spirit lingered; there was a tiny, thatched "god house" in the Valul household area on Falalap; and an immaculate, sanded circular altar as part of the Weluar household area. We called Arueligar the "high priest" because he had the highest ecclesiastical authority on the island, officiating at the few religious ceremonies we observed. Husky, handsome Truesai was his designated successor.

Ted, both in 1948 and in 1953, devoted much time to collecting notes on religious beliefs. He felt that these beliefs were steadily weakening, that he could notice a difference in this respect between his 1948 and 1953 visits. The gods, however, were still with us in 1953; alus, spirits, who haunted certain places, governed various natural events, and interfered for good or evil in the affairs of men. Ted collected a list of nine high gods, and of dozens of lesser spirits. He found, for instance, twenty-seven different alus concerned with different matters in connection with navigation and canoe building—though these, to be sure, are basic activities, much subject to divine guidance in any maritime culture.

My impression, however, based mostly on Ted's writings, notes and comments, is that the Ifalukians were far from having an organized theology. The accounts of divine affairs that Ted got from Arueligar and from the chiefs did not always agree; and most people apparently gave little thought to such matters, leaving them to the chiefs and the specialists. The alus were present, all right, but accepted as a part of the natural order of things: the spirits that every folk find in the world around them.

The vast majority of the alus were spirits of the dead. No one died while I was on Ifaluk, but Ted and Mel Spiro observed four deaths during their 1948 stay. They have described these in their book on Ifaluk: the intense preoccupation on the part of friends and relatives with trying to save a seriously ill person by every natural or supernatural means, the nightly wailing chants, the great seriousness surrounding possible death, and the abrupt relaxation of this seriousness once death has occurred, once the alus has left the body. They ascribe this attitude to the firm belief in the continuity of the soul.

The body of the dead, however, is given ceremonial treatment: the face is painted red, a new loin-cloth or skirt is put on, and then the corpse is wrapped in seemingly endless coils of rope, weighted with stones, and taken out to sea for burial. The canoe used for this then cannot be touched for four days, four being in general the magic number on Ifaluk.

The alus, the spirits of the dead, are sometimes benevolent and sometimes malevolent, apparently depending on the character of the person from whom they came. The malevolent spirits cause all sorts of trouble, including most kinds of illness. Mel Spiro, in his psychological studies of the Ifalukians, found fear of alus to be dominating both consciously and subconsciously. We had no encounters with alus, but we didn't seek any, and the attitude toward alus of the young men who worked with us seemed to be largely ritual, but we did not try to probe into their psychology.

In theory the dances, then, were designed to please the alus, both the high gods and the ordinary spirits. The elaborate ur dances which required these endless nightly rehearsals, were surely for the high gods; but all of the alus, like all of the people, must have enjoyed them. The rehearsals finally ended in the big show, which was held on July 22nd, at midday in the schoolhouse clearing.

Don and I were off taking advantage of a low tide to work on profiles of the reef when a messenger came to tell us the dance was about to start. When we got there the men had already formed into a line along the north margin of the clearing. They were all dressed up, with bows of the ivory-like unfolded coconut leaves on arms and legs, with coconut-leaf skirts over loin-cloths, with necklaces of flowers and of the greenish-ivory coconut leaves, with garlands of flowers, and surmounting all, a block of pith over the forehead, wrapped in red paper and tinfoil (from cigarette packages) and bearing a cluster of tall white feathers (perhaps from the fairy terns; but more probably and prosaically from chickens). Faces were marked with red turmeric, a streak of red along the jawline, and dabs on the cheeks and arms.

They put on a fine show. Some of the pieces were songs or chants, with an accompaniment of stamping and clapping. Others involved more complicated gesturings and posturings. In one, two men standing with outstretched arms pantomimed man-of-war birds—tilting, soaring and gliding—while the rest knelt facing each other, chanting the story. This went on for nearly an hour, with the three of us too busy with cameras and recording machine to really appreciate what was going on. Then there was an intermission. Arueligar, the high priest, distributed the two cases of corned beef and the two cartons of cigarettes we had donated for the occasion. Dancers and onlookers refreshed themselves by drinking coconuts. Then the dance was resumed, this time by the women, who formed their line along the west margin of the clearing. Their dress was similar to that of the men, except that of course they wore lava-lavas, not loin-cloths, under their coconut-leaf skirts.

Ted was interested to discover that two of the dances performed by the women were new—a concrete demonstration that the traditional form of the ur dance does not necessarily impose traditional subjects. One of the new dances, turning on a poem composed by Letaweriur, Yani's wife, concerned the first coming of the Americans to the island. It was a very long chant, recounting in detail the appearance of the first ship, the delivery of an official document, the nature of America and the Americans, and the like. Ted's translation of the opening stanza is:

> *Now all our women rejoice;*
> *Now the Americans have come.*
> *This is pleasing to the chiefs.*
> *They have given us a paper.*
> *This place is to rise;*
> *This island is to be lifted up.*
> *The chiefs say we are to dance.*
> *We will dance, we will rejoice!*
> *This very month, for this is a good year!* Ei!
> *The Japanese are gone.*
> *We did not like their rough ways.*
> *The gods have been good to us;*
> *Now our crops are safe.*
> *The Americans talk kindly. . . .*

When the women's dance was over, the people scattered into small groups—made up by family, by household, or by friendship—for the feast. Perhaps "feast" is too strong a word, since there was nothing unusual about the food except our corned beef. But always, after a communal activity of any kind, there was a communal meal. I drifted from group to group taking pictures and eating a snack of breadfruit with this friend, a hunk of taro with that, and letting them play the always-amusing game of peering at one another through the sights of my Graphic camera.

The day was shot as far as "work" for us was concerned. By the time we had got film and notes taken care of, we were ready for our afternoon swim in the lagoon in front of the Fan Nap.

From the beginning, we had formed a habit of going for a swim in the lagoon toward the end of the afternoon. Many people on Ifaluk bathed in the lagoon in late afternoon, so we were right in line with local custom. As an old Floridian, I really preferred swimming in the bright sun of mid-day and I tried to make our lagoon schedule as early in the afternoon as I could; but what with one thing or another, we often didn't get into the water until rather late.

We always wore goggles. I wonder now why anyone ever goes swimming without goggles. Man, under water, is blind without them. In many places, to be sure, there is little to see; but one can never be sure of this without trying. And in the lagoon at Ifaluk there were unending marvels to be looked at.

We were caught at first by the sheer pleasure of drifting around, exclaiming at the forms of the corals and of the colors of the fish. Then we got to thinking that if we were to spend an hour or so in the water every afternoon, we might as well be trying to make some systematic observations.

The fish, we noticed, paid very little attention to us. Apparently a large brown object of human shape plopped into their environment had no connotation of danger. The fish went on about their business as usual, indifferent to the observer. The contrast with the land, where birds and mammals clearly regard observing man as a potential enemy, was great. We didn't have to resort to field glasses or blinds—we could just float pleasantly on the surface and watch the fish. In coral seas, at least, fish watching seems to me to have it all over bird watching, though I doubt whether I would be so enthusiastic about fish watching in colder waters.

We had aqualung equipment, but this was for Bob Rofen to use in his fish collecting in the fall. We didn't touch it because the supply of compressed air was very limited, and anyway we were unfamiliar with the equipment. We felt no need for deep diving, though. There was plenty to observe close to the surface, and we had "schnorkel" breathing tubes, which were useful if you wanted to keep your eye on the fish.

If we were going to be scientific and systematic about our daily swim, the first thing to do, we decided, would be to make a map of the swimming area, so we could tell where we were. The coral in the lagoon grew in large, irregular clumps which I called "coral heads" though they are more properly called "reef knolls" or "patch reefs." These were separated by open areas in which the bottom was clean, white sand.

The coral heads near the shore grew to a height where they were just awash at low tides. The tops of these were flat, and the coral was dead except around the margins. In deeper water, the "heads" were rounded and they occurred scattered everywhere over the lagoon floor as far out as we could see, peering into the crystal water.

The coral formations in shoal water showed up plainly on our aerial photographs as irregular dark patches, and from these I tried sketching the formations directly in front of the Fan Nap, where our fish watching activities were concentrated. We subsequently checked and modified the map on the spot with the row boat, and in the end got a pretty accurate picture of this bit of the lagoon.

Landscape (or seascape) features, to be remembered, need names, so we decided we should name the reef formations in the swimming area. First to be commemorated were our wives. Two prominent and complicated contiguous masses of coral, fairly near shore, were named Izzie (for Isabela) and Nancy by Abbott and Bates respectively. Various tributary fragments broken off from these masses were given names after Abbott and Bates children. Ted selected a pleasant, rather isolated and well-rounded head to name after Marie, with Nani, his daughter, somewhat farther out in the same line, and his son David off to the right.

A central group of reefs was named after the five chiefs of Ifaluk. A large and rather sterile mass near shore presented a problem in naming which Ted neatly solved by suggesting Beldame Flats, for the slightly wacky old lady who persisted in making eyes at him during evening dance rehearsals.

Out beyond and to the north of these discrete coral heads lay a great submerged mass of dead coral, which we decided to call the continent of Moo. Moo had a complex topography, with southern and northern outposts and an octopus point, only intermittently inhabited by octopuses during the summer. A great deal of my time was spent floating over the southern outpost of Moo where a big red squirrel fish (*Holocentrus spinifer* to ichthyologists) seemed to get as much pleasure out of watching me as I got out of watching him.

Each coral formation was staked out into a series of territories by little Pomocentrid fish, called "lejoc" by the Ifalukians. The lejoc were only about three inches long, but their belligerence in defending their territories was in no way proportional to their size. We spent a lot of time teasing them. A foot, a hand, any new and foreign object intruded into the territory always caused great indignation—was always the object of fierce attack.

Each fish defended a roughly circular territory two or three feet in diameter, with boundaries marked by features of the coral landscape, and with a centrally located crevice or hole where the lejoc would lurk when not warding off intruders.

Biologists define a "territory" as an area defended by an individual, a pair, or a group, against intrusion by others of the same species. Many kinds of mammals, birds, reptiles and fish show territorial behavior, though until recently the matter had been little studied in fish, and there is still a great deal to be learned. The lejoc were clearly territorial in the strict sense, individuals clinging to the same area day after day and defending it against intrusion. My big red *Holocentrus* may also have been showing territorial behavior, since he (or she?) stayed in the same small area off Moo all summer. But I never noticed the *Holocentrus* showing aggressive behavior. Perhaps the outpost of Moo was a "home range" rather than a "territory" for this individual: the difference would depend on behavior in relation to another *Holocentrus* swimming into the area, a situation that I never had a chance to observe.

The water was full of marvels. Don had a category of what he

called "unlikely animals"—animals he never would have thought of if
he had been in charge of animal design. Any one of the three of us,
cruising around with our goggles, would be likely to shout to the
others to come see some new marvel he had just discovered for the
first time.

I remember the afternoon Ted called out "come look at this—here
is a helicopter fish!"

Sure enough there was a sort of squat fish hovering in mid-water
near Marie (Ted was apt to do his fish watching near the coral head
named after his wife) with fins split into long narrow rays which, in
their movement, had reminded Ted of a helicopter. The fish seemed
completely indifferent to our watching; presently it went into forward
gear and moved slowly and sedately off.

We looked through the fish books and presently made out that it
was *Pterois*, a "scorpion fish" or "lion fish." We learned that the pro-
truding spines were poisonous, which probably accounted for its calm
indifference. We subsequently saw these fish several times in our
swimming area, but they were not among the regular, territorial inhabitants.

The synaptid sea-cucumber was another unlikely animal. Most sea-
cucumbers have a reasonably cucumber-like form (though one kind
on Ifaluk achieved an almost watermelon-like size). The synaptids,
however, are long, slender, snake-like affairs. The species in our swimming area had a bright, almost black-and-white checkered pattern
that reminded me of some of the South American vipers like the fer-
de-lance. Stretched out from under a coral head, the sea-cucumber
looked for all of the world like a fer-de-lance crawling out from under
a rock. Only, when you looked closely, you saw not the menacing,
triangular head of the viper, but instead, where the head should be,
a rather silly-looking tuft of waving plumes. And when you picked
this unlikely animal up, you found, not firm flesh, but a limp, tissue-
paper-like affair. I always thought of them as the tissue paper fer-de-
lances of the coral heads.

Don thought that the giant clams should be included among the
unlikely animals, but he was looking at them as a zoologist, thinking
of their unlikely physiology and structure. The giant clams (*Tridacna*)

of the Ifaluk lagoon were not really giant, perhaps because people found them and ate them before they had time to reach an unlikely size. To a non-zoologist, they didn't look unusual, except for the lovely colors of the margins of the partly-opened shell and of the flesh of the animal disclosed within.

Don gave me the following explanation of the unlikely physiology of the clams (in terms of the studies of C. M. Yonge on the Tridacna of the Great Barrier Reef of Australia):

"The animal has thousands of microscopic plants, single-celled algae, in its blood. The part of the body of the clam, exposed to the sun when the shell is open, bears hundreds of tiny lenses that focus the light into pools of blood below the skin, turning the superficial tissues into a sort of greenhouse. The algae in the blood are transposed from here and digested in the blood stream in the vicinity of the gut and "liver," providing a part of the clam's diet. The rest of the Tridacna's food is assorted small plankton, filtered from the water by the gills and taken in through the mouth. Algal food digested in the blood leaves fecal wastes there—in effect the beast is defecating in its blood stream. How to get rid of the fecal wastes in this unlikely place?

"The animal, like other clams, has a pair of kidneys; in other clams these excrete nitrogenous wastes from protein breakdown. But in Tridacna these nitrogenous wastes are picked up quickly by the algae and used as a fertilizer. Tridacna's urine is almost pure sea water. But the animal has found a 'new' use for its kidneys—each acts as a sort of accessory anus to eliminate the fecal wastes left in the blood by algae digestion there. The 'farming' operation has involved complex physiological changes affecting the whole organism."

We think of molluscs as slow, deliberate animals, but these *Tridacnas* can close their shells with extraordinary speed and decision. One of our amusements was to poke things at the clams to watch the suddenness with which they could snap shut. It is quite believable that the big ones could catch a diver's foot and hold him until he drowned —a standard hazard now in Pacific movies.

Don dedicated quite a lot of time to octopus watching. Octopus Point, along the west coast of the continent of Moo, got its name from a small octopus that made headquarters there the first few weeks of the summer. Just about the time that we had decided that this octopus had a permanent home there, it disappeared and our daily checks would reveal only the empty hole. Then Don found another small octopus living in a hole in the center of the coral we named after Maroligar.

The octopuses were suspicious creatures, and while they would often be partially outside when first found, they would slowly withdraw into the recesses of their holes under the steady gaze of the observer. There was always a pile of small coral fragments outside the hole, and as an octopus retreated, these fragments were pulled in by the sucker-covered arms to block the entrance—except that generally a small peep-hole was left, framing a watchful octopus eye.

The area around the hole on Maroligar reef was littered with debris from the meals of the octopus: empty shells, claws and legs from the crabs it had eaten. Don picked up all of these and saved them—a food record on the octopus. Every day he would find the remains of more crabs, so that he got a record of the diet of this crab-loving octopus over a period of several weeks.

Then, one day, the hole on Maroligar was empty, and it remained empty for quite a while. Thus we got the impression that these octopuses would make headquarters in one place for days, or weeks, but that they did not stay permanently in any one place, did not establish "territories" the way so many of the other lagoon inhabitants did.

I only once saw an octopus swimming in the daytime. I wouldn't have seen this if it hadn't moved—a piece of a brown coral mass I was looking at suddenly gave a few convulsive movements and then shot off, jet fashion, with trailing tentacles, to the next coral head where it stopped, again blending perfectly into the background. I swam slowly toward the place where it had disappeared, but just as I got near enough so that I could distinguish octopus from coral, it took off again, this time disappearing into the depths of the lagoon.

I have been writing glibly about "coral" and "coral heads." Actually, these patch reefs were built up of a wide variety of lime-secreting organisms, many of them not true corals. We picked one of the patch reefs, Maroligar, and tried to make a map of the different kinds of organisms that were contributing to its structure. We thought this would be simple and easy, since Maroligar was a small patch reef about six yards long and a couple of yards wide. It turned out, however, to be a complicated operation, which kept Don and me busy for many hours.

Much of the trouble was technical—mostly the problem of working in the water with dry materials. When we had got an outline map made, we decided to spot the different kinds of coral and coral-like organisms on our map with colored pencils. But the colors, when wet, would blur! We had a canvas-covered inner-tube that served as a raft. We would tow mapping gear and towels on this, out to position. Then I would stand up, on some convenient part of Maroligar, dry my hands, and start trying to mark down the corals as Don, diving around with goggles, called them to me. He would come periodically to peer at my map, point with dripping finger to where I had the thing wrong, and with this well-placed drip of water that bit of my map would really be spoiled. Or I would try to move, and slip, splashing water over everything. At times we got completely fed up with the project, but we kept on and finally got a reasonable map that, with all of the different colors, was almost as pretty as Maroligar itself.

CHAPTER VII

RADIO IFALUK

FISH watching in the lagoon went on all summer, a sort of daily recreation, interrupted only by bad weather. We were serious enough in our wish to learn as much as we could about what went on in the lagoon, but since it was always there, conveniently at our doorstep, there did not seem to be great urgency about carefully scheduling its study.

The outer reef, the sea-rim of the atoll, was another matter. Work there depended on the tides. The outer, growing margin of the reef was about a hundred yards off shore, with the intervening area coral flats, exposed or barely awash at low tide. The tide tables predicted a series of particularly low tides at morning and midday hours for this part of the Pacific during the latter part of July, so Don and I concentrated on studies of the seaward side of the atoll ring during this period of favorable conditions. We wanted to find out what organisms lived there, and how they were distributed over the flats between the beach and the surf line at the reef edge.

Don and I were about this business on the morning of July 23rd when we were interrupted by Bakal running down the beach, all excited and yelling "Ship coming, Ship coming." Maybe it was the trade ship of the Trust Territory, which had long been expected on its semiannual round to collect copra.

When we got back across the island, the ship was steaming along just beyond tiny Elangalap, heading toward the pass into the lagoon. Everyone agreed that it was the trade ship. Ted dug out the bags of silver dollars and half-dollars so we could make cash gifts to the people who had helped us most—Tom, Bakal, Yani, Tony. He also made a sort of symbolic and official present of cash to each of the chiefs, as this seemed the most practical way of reciprocating for the hospitality of the island people as a whole.

Tom and some others were starting out for the ship in one of the medium-sized canoes that happened to be in the water, and asked us to come along. But with the unusual load the canoe started to leak badly, and we had not gone very far before the impracticality of the expedition became clear. Bakal in the meanwhile had started out in the ungainly rowboat—the much maligned BWUP—and Don and Ted shifted to this unpicturesque but safe form of transport. I was feeling resentful about the whole business—this seemingly constant interruption of our peaceful summer by intruding ships—and I could see no reason for going to all of the bother of going out to visit the darn thing. So I went back to the Fan Nap and sulked.

Don and Ted reported that the ship was another converted Army AK, a twin of the NETTLE that had brought us to the island. A representative of the Trust Territory on Yap was on board, and he and the captain were having lunch when they arrived, so Don and Ted joined them. Don, when he came back, made a lot of noise about two heaping bowls of chocolate ice cream that he ate; but even this didn't dent my resentment about Western civilization steaming in and anchoring just off the pass into our lagoon.

Presently a launch-load of visitors from the ship turned up at the landing beach before the Fan Nap. There was Mr. Hirsch, the government representative from Yap, a pleasant-seeming and serious-minded man with a master's degree in Political Science. With him came an official interpreter—a young man from one of the neighboring atolls who had acquired fluent English, trousers, shirt, shoes, dark glasses and a rather supercilious attitude toward the crudities of backward places like Ifaluk. There was a Catholic missionary, Father Corrigan, looking very relaxed with sunburn, shorts and Japanese sandals. One family on Ifaluk had been converted, I judge by way of relatives on the atoll of Wolei, and this family had built a little thatched chapel in their household area. There was a clean-looking and intelligent young agricultural expert, Mr. Kim, raised and trained in Hawaii, working for the Trust Territory government. And there was a short, dark, alert radio mechanic, native of Yap, along with boxes containing a radio receiving and sending set complete with generator run with a gasoline motor.

During our week in Guam on the way to Ifaluk, we had of course gone around to call at the offices of the Trust Territory government there—to meet the people, to thank them for their many courtesies, and to ask if there were any special way in which we could be directly helpful during our Ifaluk residence. In the course of this conversation, the problems of communication among the small, scattered islands of the Territory came up. There was no way of advising the people, on an island like Ifaluk, of the schedule of the trade ship; no way of knowing when some emergency might arise on the island; no way of getting advance information about possible needs before the trade ship came.

The Territory government had some war surplus radio equipment: but the problems of installation and of training operators were very difficult. Would we help them set up a station on Ifaluk, and train some of the local people to operate it? It might, incidentally, be a great convenience for us, if some emergency happened to arise. We pointed out our vast and complete ignorance of radio operation—but this, it appeared, was no drawback, since the equipment would have fixed adjustments. So we agreed to do anything we could and then forgot about it. But here now was the radio, a solid reality out of the Western world.

It didn't take much discussion to decide that the "schoolhouse" was the proper place to install the radio. So the mechanic from Yap got busy, with the fascinated assistance of practically all of the young men of Ifaluk, stringing an antenna from the peak of the schoolhouse roof to a breadfruit tree on the edge of the clearing, setting up the generator as far from the sending and receiving set as the cable would allow, so that the racket from the gasoline motor would not drown out the radio sounds.

He finally got everything arranged to his satisfaction. The peace of the atoll was shattered by the roar of the motor and the mechanic took up the microphone and started fiddling with the imposing array of dials on the sending panel.

"Radio Yap, Radio Yap; this is Radio Ifaluk calling; Radio Ifaluk calling Radio Yap. Over."

Nothing came through but the crash and bang of static. More fiddling with the dials, more calls to Radio Yap. Finally a few words came back through the static and a faint contact was established.

We had to decide on a schedule for contacts. We thought that once a week would be plenty of communication, and arrangements were made that we would call Yap regularly on Monday evenings at 8 o'clock our time. The mechanic fixed the setting on the proper wave length and explained the details of operation to Don, who would be in charge of the communications department. Don practiced exchanging a few remarks with the operator on Yap and then the whole thing was shut up, to be tackled again on the following Monday night.

The installation of the radio naturally caused a great deal of excitement—Ifaluk now caught up in the network of the modern world. The young men could be heard everywhere practicing the magic words "Radio Yap, calling Radio Yap; this is Radio Ifaluk. Over." Everyone wanted to be the radio operator, which might well present us with a problem in diplomacy. Yani, with the most practice in English, and the most studious temperament of the younger men, seemed to be the logical choice.

The Ifalukians were very disappointed to find that the ship had no trade goods to sell, and was not picking up copra. They had accumulated quite a bit of copra with no way of disposing of it until the trade ship would come to pick it up; and they were also in need of outside supplies. Their biggest desire was for tobacco. Every adult on the island seemed to have the smoking habit, and this puzzled me in view of the difficulties of getting and keeping supplies. I couldn't help but remember the trouble I had had learning to smoke—because it was the "right thing" to do—and the trouble I now had in trying to quit. I had thought that the "lift" from nicotine was perhaps primarily imagined, and that the real basis of the habit was nervousness. But observation of the Ifalukians didn't bear this out.

The old men could remember their first encounter with smoking—

the men on the German ships that occasionally visited the island "eating fire." But they must have quickly and easily found some real value in this fire-eating habit, judging by its hold on the people in our day. They really preferred the strong twist tobacco put out for the Pacific trade, which they cut up and wrapped in dried banana leaf for smoking. The tobacco in this heavy, rope-like form, was certainly more practical for handling under island conditions than the manufactured cigarettes were; but we found, on trying, that the stuff was too strong for us. They accepted our cigarettes willingly enough, and we used considerable numbers every day, since they were among the few things we had that could serve as daily symbols of friendship and goodwill and appreciation of the constant courtesy of all of the atoll inhabitants.

The children did not smoke—I judge their elders considered it wasn't good for them, which contrasts with the situation in some other societies. Ted, however, had the brilliant idea of bringing along a considerable quantity of hard candy for the children; this was a great success. I always carried a packet in my pocket, which was very likely the explanation of my great popularity with the small-fry of the island. It meant, incidentally, that I always had a ready supply of subjects to lend human interest to photographs, though at first it was a little difficult to persuade them not to pose. And, to the end of the summer, some camera-hogging five-year-old was always liable to plop unexpectedly into the field of the camera. Though I must say that in general they were remarkably good about my sign directions as to where to go and what to do when being photographed.

But to get back to the question of trade goods. Aside from tobacco, most of the things that the Ifalukians wanted were quite practical. We made out a list to give to the government representative of things the people said they wanted: big steel adze blades for hewing out planks for canoes or beams for houses; short-bladed machetes (it is curious how societies differ in the preferences in dimensions of bush-knives); wooden swimming goggles; pots and pans, especially big ones. They also wanted beads of all kinds, and red face paint of a sort made from turmeric—apparently an ancient trade specialty of Yap and Palau in Micronesia.

The men got all dressed up for the "ur" dance; but flower garlands, made by the women, were also everyday wear.

The children, though "secure," were far from obnoxious —in fact it would be difficult to imagine a more delightful bunch of kids.

ABOVE A big sea-going canoe was being built in the Falepenach canoe house.

BELOW Fagolier, the paramount chief, took an active part in all work, whether hewing planks or weaving fish nets.

Steel certainly has been a great gift from the West to these island cultures. Cutting trees, clearing brush, hewing out planks for canoes, must have been a tedious process with only shell tools. Pots, pans, buckets and bottles were also an important contribution to a culture that had no clay for pottery, that had to depend on coconut shells, gourds and wooden bowls for containers. The list of contributions, after these, became less certain. I would give mosquito netting and swimming goggles a very high priority. Mosquitoes were certainly one of the important flaws in paradise, not because they carried any disease in this environment, but because of nuisance value from sheer abundance. Yani said that he had heard that in the old days, before they had nets, the people kept smudge-fires going in the houses and even so could sometimes only find peace by paddling out to the middle of the lagoon. The goggles, of course, for these amphibious people, were a great help in the daily chore (or sport?) of fish spearing.

About half of the Ifalukian men wore loin-cloths made of trade cloth, the others continuing to use the traditional material woven from fiber of the textile Hibiscus despite the discomfort involved in breaking them in. None of the women used trade cloth for their skirts. Fish nets of various sorts, and canoe sails, were still woven locally. Except for mosquito netting, I could not see that the West had much to offer in the way of textile products.

We discussed the problems, for Ifaluk, of outside contact off and on all summer. The island, protected by its insignificant size and distance from major centers, had somehow escaped the "contamination" from Western culture that appeared to have had such unfortunate consequences in many areas of the Pacific. In areas of close contact, the people seemed to have lost integrity, self-reliance, independence, without, as far as one could see, any corresponding material or spiritual gain. As they became dependent on trade goods, they became dependent on finding some means of raising the cash to buy the trade goods, in a region not really overflowing with trade resources. The chief thing they had to sell was their labor: this meant, then, that instead of "working" to make their canoes and their clothes, they worked to earn the money to buy them. We couldn't see how this was a gain, especially since the imported product often did not seem as well adapted to the local needs as the home-made product was.

Yet it would not be right artificially to "protect" the Ifalukian culture, like wildlife carefully maintained on some reserve. The Ifalukians had so far shown a remarkable integrity in maintaining their traditional culture, which seemed to us so admirably adapted to their environment. But they also liked the idea of "progress" and liked the gadgets of the West, as they so clearly showed in their enthusiasm about the installation of Radio Ifaluk. The problem, it seemed to us, was how to help them get the positive values of our own culture without, at the same time, undermining the very real values of their own. We could argue endlessly about that, and often did.

But the particular contact with the West by way of the Trust Territory ship on July 23rd was brief enough. The government representative, the priest, the agriculturist, the radio mechanic had all finished their business by the middle of the afternoon and we went down to the lagoon shore to watch them board the launch and head out across the lagoon to the ship anchored just outside the pass. They were pleasant and intelligent people, certainly, and we were glad of the chance to observe an official visitation. We hoped though, that if any more ships turned up, they would at least bring us mail—so far none of them had.

We dropped back into our routine—selfishly thankful that the visitors had left early enough so that we didn't miss our regular afternoon period of fish watching. Then Yani came in with the day's food record for the Falepenach household. The fourteen people of the household had used five pounds of breadfruit, seven pounds and fourteen ounces of pulach, three bottles of hachi, four pieces of smoked bonito (with an estimated total weight of four pounds) and they had used the meat of one ripe coconut.

Yani and Don fell into one of their long discussions, which were rapidly giving Yani a considerable fluency in English. This time, according to Don's journal entry, the talk, starting with the food record, went on into the subject of "food chains"—man eating big fish, big fish eating smaller fish, small fish eating all sorts of tiny animals which in turn lived on the microscopic plants of the sea.

I don't know how far Don got with the food chain—whether he

managed to explain photosynthesis and the microscopic algae of the lagoon plankton—but he did note in the journal that Yani got the idea fast enough. Yani always seemed to get the idea. I often thought that but for the accidents of geography, economics and culture, there went a Harvard Ph.D. Not that a Ph.D. would have been of any use to Yani; but a realization of the accidental basis of their learning might be a healthy corrective for some Ph.Ds. *88370*

A few days after the visit of the government ship, we were introduced to another element in the Ifalukian diet—the land crabs, called rahom (*Cardiosoma*). The holes of these crabs could be seen everywhere through the boondocks, but the crabs themselves were rarely out during the daytime. Yani had told us that at this time of year (May, June and July) the crabs come out in great numbers on three nights of full moon each month (which would mean high evening tides) and go down to the beach on the ocean side of the islands to spawn. At such times they are caught in large numbers for food.

The Ifalukians and the crabs both seemed to be pretty good at timing this operation, though it was easier to understand the time sense of the Ifalukians than that of the crabs. Ted had gone into the matter of the calendar of Ifaluk pretty thoroughly on the occasion of his first visit to the island. He found no word for "year" and no method of keeping track of the passage of years. There were, however, two seasons, which would have added up to make a year: vang, the season of the easterly trade winds, and rag, the season of calms and variable, mostly westerly, winds. Rag, extending from about April to November, was considerably the longer season. The people also followed the changes of the moon closely. They had a word for each of the twelve lunar months, and also a separate name for each night of the lunar cycle. The nights of full moon in the first part of the period of westerly winds would thus be clearly enough distinguished in the vocabulary of Ifaluk.

About the timing of the crabs, we can only guess. Certainly many biological phenomena have marvellously precise timing arrangements, much more precise than the spawning of the crabs on Ifaluk. Internal physiological rhythms are involved, often regulated by some particular factor in the environment such as length of day or temperature. In the mid-tropics, where environmental conditions of all sorts are remarkably constant through the year, few experiments have been made to determine what factors actually govern the timing of the flowering of plants and the spawning of animals. With these crabs, the basic rhythm, whereby eggs were matured once a year, was probably physiological; the trigger for spawning, whereby the crabs went down to the water on only a few particular nights, might have been a response to either the tide or the light. The crab holes on the land probably went down to water level, so that water in the holes would rise and fall with the tides; and the crabs, coming out to forage every night, might also easily react to the changing intensity of moonlight.

We went over to the outer shore of Falalap for our first crabbing expedition—the crabs were more abundant there than on our home base of Falarik. It was a bright moonlight night, and we half expected to find the beach teeming with pregnant crabs struggling to release their burdens of ripe eggs in the sea, with people striding through the mass to scoop them up for food.

We found, instead, a completely peaceful scene. The beach, in the soft light, seemed at first deserted, and the only sounds were from a gentle surf where the swells of the Pacific were breaking on the outer reef, a hundred yards off shore, and from the lapping of the secondary waves that reached up among the rocks of the beach at this high tide. We carried flashlights, and with these we soon made out groups of people huddled in the dark shade of the beach vegetation, each group 150 feet or so from the next, all very quiet. We quickly realized the flashlights were a disturbing element, and switched them off, going as quietly as we could on down the beach until we found an unoccupied stretch in which our party could settle down.

The crab hunting, we soon found, was a contest in vigilance between the crabs and the people. The crabs would sidle down to the edge of the vegetation and lurk there behind logs, rocks or palm fronds, for all the world as though they were sizing up the chances for an undisturbed dash across the open gravel slope, perhaps fifteen feet wide at this high tide. When they ventured out into the open, gravel beach, they could be seen, as moving dark objects, perhaps thirty feet away. Don watched one crab go into the water where it stayed, close to the shore, for about two minutes, in which time it would have released many thousands of free-swimming larvae from the egg masses attached under its abdomen.

We caught about fifty crabs in two hours, some of them while they were making this dash across the beach, others by foraging among the debris along the vegetation line. The crabs had powerful claws and even the most expert catchers sometimes got cuts; the trick was to get them by the back of the shell, where the crabs could not reach with their claws.

As the evening progressed, the beach became a line of tiny fires, where the various groups of people were roasting the freshly caught crabs. The egg masses were the most highly prized part, with a flavor not unlike that of shad roe; and there was a considerable amount of very tasty meat not only in the claws and legs, but in the body itself.

We were too infected by the spirit of the place, that first night, to be scientific. We caught crabs, we ate them, and we absorbed as much of the atmosphere of the moon-drenched beach as the ever-pestering mosquitoes would allow. But next day we realized that we had to get more clear-cut data about this rahom phenomenon. So we resolved to be scientists that night.

It was Don's evening for English class—he had taken to giving lessons every third night—so that had to be attended to first. There were about a dozen regulars now, and they squatted in a circle behind the Fan Nap in the bright light of a couple of gasoline lanterns and struggled with words and sentences for an hour or so. Usually, during the lesson period, I busied myself with field notes or journal; but this night the moonlight in the coconut grove was too much and I gave up notes to wander out and wallow in the romantic atmosphere.

Presently my musings were interrupted by an awareness that something very curious was happening to the moonlight—it was changing from a silvery to a reddish texture. The moon itself, on looking up, seemed angry and inflamed. I remember a queer feeling of panic, of fear that something had gone wrong with the orderly working of the cosmos. Within a few minutes the cause was clear enough—the black shadow of the earth began to edge into the disc of the moon. We were in the path of a total or nearly total eclipse. I called out to the English class, protected from the change by their circle of bright light, and everyone stopped to look. There were murmurings about alus, spirits, and I could well believe it in the eerie quality of the light.

Don's pedagogical instincts came to the fore, and he explained what was happening with two coffee cups and the gasoline lantern. It was reassuring and regular; but it took a little while to shake off the creepy feeling brought on by that queer, reddish moonlight. I guess I had never seen a lunar eclipse before; certainly not from a coconut grove in the South Seas. And there is something about moonlight any-way that gives plausibility to the verbal relation with lunacy.

Presently, however, Don and I pulled ourselves together and started for the ocean side of Falarik to collect crabs. We carried a pillow-case to hold our booty, and we tried to concentrate on watching the crabs, which were rather scarce on this stretch of beach on this particular night. It was hard to concentrate in the magic moonlight, now ex-tremely brilliant. We managed, somehow, to collect eight females loaded with eggs and started back with them. But the moonlight along the trail on the way home was too much for us, and we couldn't bring ourselves to weigh and measure crabs when we got back to the Fan Nap. So we put the pillow-case aside till morning and I sat for a while on a log and stared out through the palms at the silver lagoon until the mosquitoes drove me to the protection of the bed netting. Don, incurably romantic, wrote poetry in the light of the moon until some ungodly hour—the atmosphere for once making him oblivious even to the mosquitoes. (He won't let me quote the poem.)

The reality that we faced next morning was a sorry mess. The white pillow-case of crabs, which we had left for safety's sake in a wire fish trap, had turned a rich, stinking brown—we were never able to turn it white again. The crabs had torn a hole in the cloth, and most of them were out clambering over the wire of the trap. At first sight, it looked as though they had lost their egg masses, but a closer look showed that they were still there, but shrunk into a desiccated remnant of their former fruitfulness.

We had wanted to count the number of larvae produced by a single crab. We carried on, and put one of the crabs in a pan of sea water. A few tiny larvae dribbled out—nothing like the surging mass that we had hoped to see. We then washed the crab's recurved abdomen, and were rewarded by freeing immense numbers of larvae, but all of them dead. They would still serve for counting, so we strained them out with a plankton net, and preserved them for some future rainy day.

Then there was the matter of the food content of the crab. We killed four specimens by dropping them in boiling water; then, directly they were dead, we weighed them. Later in the day, after they had been cooked, Ted, Don and I all dedicated ourselves to getting out the crab meat, separating the meat and the trash for separate weighing. We were really being precise and scientific about this aspect of the local diet. The four crabs, according to my notebook, had an aggregate weight of 1 lb. 7.5 oz. The meat, so painstakingly pulled out of claws, legs and body, had a total weight of nine ounces, so it seemed that there was about two ounces of food in the average rahom.

So we continued our routines of food studies, mapping, reef transects, and afternoon fish watching in the lagoon. But we were no longer isolated in the Pacific; we had Radio Ifaluk installed in the schoolhouse and on Monday night at eight o'clock everyone trooped over to the schoolhouse for the first broadcast.

I took over the generator and after a pull or two on the crank, with just the right delicate touch on the choke, the motor started up with a roar. Don switched on the sending set, picked up the mike in a professional-looking way, and started calling "Radio Yap, Radio Yap; this is Radio Ifaluk calling Radio Yap. Over."

But nothing came back except static—a hell of a lot of static. We fiddled with such dials as we dared, but still only static. I hurried back to the Fan Nap, turned on our battery receiving set, and picked up Radio Ifaluk clearly enough, so we were sending all right. But nothing came back.

I don't know how disappointed the Ifalukian population was. They may have enjoyed the stir and the noise, and the chance of several people to practice with the mike. It seemed a flop to us, though. We kept on trying all summer. A week later, we did manage to hear Yap faintly, and to get the suggestion that it might be better to try midday contact, when there would be less static. We tried that, but with no surer results than before.

At any rate, we tried every week, and various young men got practice with the motor and the microphone and Ifaluk thus very uncertainly and haphazardly made its start toward fitting into the communications network of the modern world.

CHAPTER VIII

WELL DIGGING

I BECAME increasingly conscious, toward the end of July, of how little time I had to learn about Ifaluk. The ship to pick up Ted and me was due on September 12th: six weeks away, a month away, two weeks away. The time gap narrowed frighteningly. Yet, curiously, the days themselves were so full of things, so different each from the last, that they lengthened out delightfully. Time was terrifying only in relation to that fixed endpoint.

The ship that came to pick us up would drop Arnow, the hydrologist; Tracey, the geologist; Rofen, the fish man and Bayer, the student of marine invertebrates. Rofen and Bayer would be staying, with Don, until the middle of November. Since these three were all marine biologists, it seemed logical to leave most marine studies for that final period, and for Don and me to concentrate on land studies during the period I was around. This was hard, because I was fascinated by the lagoon, the reef and the sea and wanted to learn all I could about them from Don. But we were reasonably conscientious and spent a considerable portion of our time collecting plants and insects and trying to describe vegetation.

Our ecological survey, during the latter half of the summer, was closely connected with the progress of well digging. The well-digging operation was for the benefit of Ted Arnow. We had promised to have a series of wells ready for him, dug at strategic locations to give cross-sections on each of the islands, so that he could study the behavior of the ground water on the atoll.

Tom was made superintendent of well digging, and the project was finally started on August 4th with a series of four wells across Falarik near the north end. In all, Arnow and Don had planned three such series across Falarik, and other series to give cross-sections on Falalap and Ella.

Arnow had left a supply of shovels for the well-digging operation, and Tom organized a gang of eight men. We arranged to pay them in cash at the standard rate established by the Trust Territory government for labor—which would give them money to spend if and when that trade ship turned up with things to sell.

The Ifalukians were incapable of doing anything in a slapdash manner, and they ended up by digging most elegant wells. First they would dig a square pit, about eight feet on a side, down to a depth a few inches above water level, making a clean, flat bottom and giving a slight slope to the sides. In the center of this, they would dig a round hole, about two feet in diameter, going down a foot or so below water level, and neatly lined with stones to prevent cave-ins. This resulted not only in a fine set of stations for Arnow's water studies, but also in a neat series of soil profiles for a description of the land stratification of the atoll.

Our vegetation survey of the atoll was roughly tied in with the well digging: we had, anyway, to locate the strategic points for the wells and to show interest and appreciation of the progress of the digging, which took us off the reef and out into the boondocks regularly. And it was logical to make cross-sections of the plant growth in the same places where cross-sections of the soil and the water level were being made.

Before the well digging started, we had accumulated a pretty fair collection of the different kinds of plants growing on the island, though we kept on the look-out for additions right up to the last day. Along with the notes on the plant specimens, we recorded the local plant names, and we used these local names for all of our field notes on vegetation. Neither Don nor I were very good botanists, though Don was familiar with some of the plants because of his long experience in Hawaii. We would have been lost, however, if we had had to depend on our knowledge of the plants, or on our ability to characterize and discriminate the species—we were able to make the studies that we did of the vegetation only because the Ifalukians knew their local flora thoroughly and because we were able to take advantage of this knowledge.

We found 119 species of "higher plants"—seed plants and ferns—growing on the atoll, and the Ifalukians had special names for all but six of these. Three of the six were grasses that they did not distinguish among—we couldn't distinguish them either—and the others were trivial plants, possibly of recent accidental introduction.

This, of course, is a very small number of plants for a region of high rainfall in the mid-tropics. A list of the plants growing wild in the vicinity of Miami, Florida, includes about 800 species; a flora of a small, coastal valley in Honduras (the flora of Lancetilla Valley, as listed by Paul Stanley) includes over 1500 species. Paul Stanley listed 1057 species of ferns and seed plants found on the island of Barro Colorado (six square miles of surface area) in Gatun Lake in the Panama Canal Zone.

The limited flora of Ifaluk is, of course, a direct consequence of the history and geography of the island. Ifaluk is an oceanic island—that is, it has never formed a part of one of the continental land masses. Continental islands—those which were once directly continuous with the neighboring continents, like the British Islands with Europe, Trinidad with South America, or Sumatra with Asia, continue to maintain the continental flora (and fauna) after they have become isolated as islands. Evolution may take a different course on the isolated island, so that in time peculiar species will develop, but the main elements present at the time of separation continue to be represented.

Oceanic islands, on the other hand, are inhabited only by plants and animals that somehow, some time, have managed to get there from the continents across the intervening seas. The biota of such islands is thus almost always limited and peculiar. Where the islands are geologically ancient, in existence for many millions of years, like the Hawaiian Islands or the Galapagos Islands, cumulative accidents may result in a considerable diversity of inhabitants. It is sometimes almost impossible to imagine how the ancestor of some animal or plant got to such islands, but in the course of millions of years the most improbable accidents gain a certain probability and almost anything may happen.

In the case of Ifaluk, however, we do not have millions of years. We know that during the (geologically) recent Ice Ages, sea levels fluctuated greatly as the continental glaciers advanced, binding up water from the sea, or retreated, releasing water. Low-lying Ifaluk has probably been a completely submerged reef within a matter of a few thousands of years. All of the plants and animals living on Ifaluk, then, have had to have some means of getting there within a comprehensible period of time.

The plants and animals, from this point of view, fall easily into three groups: those that got to Ifaluk by some "natural" means, those deliberately brought by man, and those accidentally introduced by man. I tried to sort out the 119 species of plants according to these three categories, but it turned out not to be easy. Thirty-two species were clearly always cultivated, and were equally clearly deliberate introductions by man. Plants like the seedless breadfruit and the banana species have, in fact, become utterly dependent on man, incapable of any dispersal without human intervention.

But there are many borderline cases—and one of the most puzzling of these is the coconut. Coconuts are now found everywhere on tropical beaches, but no one is really sure, for instance, whether it was originally an Old World or New World plant. The nuts can survive considerable exposure to sea water—but they are also carried and deliberately planted by man everywhere in the coastal tropics. Coconuts, to be sure, are found on many uninhabited islands, but one cannot rule out the possibility of man having landed there and planted them.

It is also, in many cases, hard to distinguish between accidental human dispersal and natural dispersal. Many plants have natural means of dispersal that enable them to get almost everywhere—spores or seeds that can be carried long distances by wind, or that stick to the feathers or feet of sea birds, or that can resist salt water and be carried by ocean currents. Such plants make up the basic beach flora of all of the scattered oceanic islands of the tropical Pacific. Others, especially the garden weeds, clearly come along with man as uninvited guests when he carries breadfruit or taro plants from one place to another. But it is beyond my power to make a clear decision in every case. Roughly, I suspect that about a third of the plants of Ifaluk got there by natural means—would be there if man had never taken to navigating—and that another third were brought by man deliberately, and the remaining third by man accidentally.

Land animals are understandably scarce on oceanic islands. On Ifaluk the Pacific rat had come along, uninvited, with man; and man had purposely brought cats and monitor lizards to try to control the rats. Pigs, chickens, dogs and cats make the complete list of purposely introduced mammals. The small lizards that were everywhere seem to have arrived by a hitch-hiking process on the ocean-going canoes.

With the insects, as with the plants, it would be hard to decide the means of arrival in each individual case. There were only two kinds of butterflies on Ifaluk, both of these powerful fliers that have spread all through Micronesia, and the dragonflies, too, presumably got to Ifaluk under their own power. I suspect, though, that a lot of the different kinds of pesky flies got to Ifaluk with the canoes.

But the insects on Ifaluk were overshadowed by the hermit crabs, which crawled in their teeming abundance, all over the island. We suspected that they filled a scavenger function which in other places would be taken over by insects. Since the insects hadn't got to Ifaluk, the hermit crabs, crawling out of the sea, found themselves without competition on land, and flourished.

I started, however, to write about plants rather than insects and hermit crabs. The high proportion of deliberately introduced plants reflected the Ifaluk interest in gardening. The Ifalukians were all gardeners, and they liked to get seeds of new plants to try out on their atoll. One household in particular, that of Buennau, had a variety of things growing in their garden found nowhere else on the atoll. I used to think that the ladies of the Buennau household, in our culture, would have been leaders in the local garden club. They were kind and cooperative, like garden-club ladies generally, and let us take little snippets of their rare plants for our collection, so we could include them in the island list.

Man obviously enough was in control of his gardens on Ifaluk, not only at Buennau but at all of the households. Gradually, as we extended our explorations and tried to map the patterns of different kinds of vegetation on the atoll, we came to have the feeling that man was the controlling factor in the vegetation everywhere. This, of course, was easily possible—perhaps inevitable—with 260 people living on a half of a square mile of land surface. But it took us a while to realize it.

I don't mean that the whole atoll surface was cultivated. In many areas, the human control was negative: man didn't care what grew at the north end of Falarik or along the boulder ridge, so he left the vegetation there alone. But the pattern, even in such cases, could only be understood in terms of human activity—or absence of human activity. Deliberate human intervention—the cutting out of unwanted trees, the selective use of wanted trees, and the planting of things like breadfruit and coconut—extended almost everywhere and could never be discounted.

We could work out the main patterns of land use on the atoll from the air photographs, coupled with our ground explorations. But we wanted more precise descriptions of sample areas. For one of these areas, we selected the trail that went almost straight across Falarik from the Fan Ni Wa canoe house, located just about half-way down the island on the lagoon shore. Four wells of Arnow's study were dug along this trail, and while the wells were being dug, Don and I struggled with the problem of how to get a cross-section of the vegetation.

I wanted to try making a diagrammatic sketch that would show the height of the trees in various places, the density of plant growth, and the like: but after one attempt, I realized that this was out of the question. Don had a better idea: we could divide the trail into twenty-meter sections and then list the plants found growing in each section, noting how common they were. I practiced to try to get a stride just a meter long so that we could measure the sections (how we wished we had a steel tape!). I managed only fairly well—it was 350 Bates strides across the island, but as I measure it now on the map, the distance was really about 360 meters.

Anyway, I strode along the trail as precisely as I could, and at every twenty strides we marked some convenient tree with a tag. Then Don and Yani retraced the trail carefully, noting, by their Ifalukian names, all of the trees and plants that grew on either side. Fifty-two different kinds of plants grew along the trail—a fair proportion of the total flora of the atoll. In trying to translate the local names into botanical names, it turns out that we neglected to collect specimens of two of these plants, so we have no scientific name for them. I wonder now how many other plants we missed: it is surprisingly difficult to get a complete list of people, plants or anything even on a spot of land as small as the atoll of Ifaluk.

Starting at the outer, ocean end of the trail, was the dense tangle of vegetation on the "boulder ridge" just back of the beach, composed of plants with wide powers of dispersal, and with ability to resist the salt spray that must cover them at every high wind. This strand vegetation is composed of about the same plants everywhere in the Western tropical Pacific: small trees like Messerschmidia, Scaevola and Pisonia; gaunt, tall-growing Pandanus; a few tough ferns and herbs, with salt-resistant vines, like the beach morning glory, that send creepers out onto the otherwise naked beach.

The land, on the ocean side of the atoll, rises steeply from the beach to reach a height of ten to fifteen feet above sea-level, fifteen or twenty yards in from the margin of the vegetation. This boulder ridge, built of coral rocks tossed up by the storms of centuries, is the highest part of every atoll. The ridge, on the Fan Ni Wa trail, was about ten yards wide; the trail then dipped down again into the heavy shade of the woods that covered the whole central part of the island. This woods, which looked wild enough to the casual glance, was composed chiefly of breadfruit (which must have been planted) and other useful trees. This was the boondocks—but with man well in control.

About two-thirds of the way across, toward the lagoon, there were numerous small swampy areas. Here, in the rich, mucky soil, taro and many kinds of flowers were grown, though these gardens still had a wild look, with no obvious signs of the careful cultivation so apparent in the big gardens in the middle of Falalap. The trail wound through this swampy area to reach, with higher ground again, the "boondock line," coming out into the open coconut grove of the lagoon margin. The lagoon park, here, was about 100 yards wide. An unusual number of garden plants got onto the list for this part of the trail because it passed by the Buennau household, where the garden-club ladies lived, before ending at the Fan Ni Wa canoe house.

Presently the three lines of wells across Falarik were finished, and the well-digging operation moved to Falalap. I might note that the crews changed with each new set of wells, so that the cash income from well digging would be equally distributed among the households of the island; the only continuity was Tom, who continued importantly as boss-man for the whole, atoll-wide operation.

We tended to neglect Falalap, though it was just as important a part of the atoll as Falarik. I suppose this was because we lived on Falarik and were essentially lazy by nature. It was just a couple of hundred yards from our headquarters at the Fan Nap to the village on Falalap, but going there meant wading the narrow, shallow pass, where the water could be well above the knees or even up to the crotch at high tide, though scarcely more than ankle deep at low tide. This was just enough of a barrier to lead us to give most of our attention to our home island. But we had to focus our interest on Falalap when the well digging moved there.

Falalap had a rather different "feel" from Falarik. For one thing, the village was largely shaded with great breadfruit trees instead of coconuts—the palms were relatively scarce except right along the shore. For another thing, one section of the large swamp that made up the middle of Falalap came right up to the edge of the village, making a topographic situation quite different from that on the narrow, drier island of Falarik.

The swamp of Falalap made it the breadbasket of the atoll. There the taros, wot and pulach, grew to perfection, and each of the atoll households had rights to definite parcels of the Falalap swamp. The work of the gardens was exclusively in the hands of the women. There was, as a matter of fact, a rule that men were not allowed in the swamps, perhaps because they would be likely to distract the women about their work. We got special permission from the chiefs, so that Yani and Bakal could go with us into the big taro patches to collect the weeds that grew there. The men weren't of much help in this environment, though—they had constantly to turn to the women for the plant names and uses.

The men in general knew remarkably little about the bwols, as the big taro swamps were called. It was a woman's world. It was a world of work, too, weeding, transplanting, harvesting in the still, sticky air of the center of Falalap, where the constant breeze that made most of the atoll so comfortable was cut out by the thick, surrounding vegetation.

Yet even in the steamy bwol I was never able to get the matter of work and play entirely straight. Cultivating the taro was a basic economic activity, clearly enough; necessary and productive work. But around the margins of the bwols, the women grew a profusion of flowers—especially hibiscus, canna, and ginger. They went out every morning to care for and harvest the taro—but they spent also a great deal of time on the flowers. And when they came back with their baskets of food for the stomach, they also carried flowers, which they wove into their beautiful maremars, as they called their garlands. Should this be called "work" too?

Falalap was an oval island, quite different in shape from long and narrow Falarik; and it had little frontage on the lagoon—sticking out, instead, into the ocean and spoiling the neat circle of the atoll reef. Falalap had its "broad highway" like Falarik, but in this case the highway made a circle of the island, completely surrounding the bwols, and giving easy access to them. We had a terrible time mapping this circum-island trail; the thing just wouldn't come out right, no matter what we did. We finally had to resort to a little judicious cheating in order to get a reasonably plausible map. The trouble apparently lay in our aerial photographs, which were not always vertical, leading to distortion.

When appropriate wells had been dug on Falalap, the operation moved to the uninhabited islet of Ella. There were no trails on Ella, so we cut one directly across the middle of the island, and marked points where three wells were to be dug. Don and Yani, by now a smooth-working team for vegetation studies, made a count of the different kinds of plants growing in the transect while I, as usual, prowled around with cameras.

We had thought that Ella would provide us with some idea of what undisturbed atoll vegetation would be like, but this turned out to be a mistake. The island was covered with a rather uniform and thick growth of small trees, chiefly of three species, *Morinda citrifolia, Allophylus timorensis* and *Premna corymbosa.* The uniformity of the vegetation was explained when Tom told us that just before the recent war, the Japanese had ordered the Ifalukians to clear Ella of all vegetation for the purpose of converting it into a coconut plantation. The Ifalukians had cleared a part of the island all right, but the Japanese power had not lasted long enough to lead to the establishment of the coconut plantation, so the vegetation that we saw was a second-growth of somewhat more than ten years standing. There were numerous coconut and breadfruit trees on Ella, but the Ifalukians paid little attention to them, since Falarik and Falalap produced all that they needed.

Apparently Ella had never been lived on—the Ifalukians said because there was no fresh water. Our well-digging operation turned up fresh water—to everyone's surprise—but we were there during the rainy season, and conditions in the dry period from December to April might be quite different.

The absence of man did make for many differences on Ella. We had hardly started cutting the trail that first day when Tom called out excitedly that he had found a coconut crab—something we had never seen on Falarik or Falalap, where the people probably didn't give these big and tasty crabs a chance to survive.

Tom's crab was in a burrow under the roots of a big Premna tree— you could get a glimpse of its big bluish legs and pincers as it shifted around in the hole. Tom collected a pile of dried palm fronds and got set to smoke the crab out, while I stood by with camera and flash-gun ready to immortalize the occasion. Tom made a fine, smoky fire, but the crab refused to budge and finally, half-cooked, was removed piecemeal.

Yani located another crab inside a hollow branch of another Premna tree—and this time was able to remove the small crab entire by chopping open the branch.

The coconut crab is a fabulous sort of animal—a giant among crustacea, a relative of the ubiquitous hermit crabs. We can certify that its reputation as perhaps the tastiest of the crustacea is also well deserved—a finer and more delicate flavor, somehow, than lobster.

Though probably the flavor is helped, when one is eating coconut crab, by the consciousness that one is eating a rare, exotic and fabled morsel.

The coconut crab has tremendously powerful claws. Whether, with these claws, it is capable of breaking open an intact coconut to get at the meat has been the subject of much argument. Tom and Yani very definitely said that crabs did open intact nuts that had fallen to the ground and they showed us the evidence—piles of thin strips of coconut fiber stripped off the nut, and beside them the tiny fragments of the hard shell. They said the crabs loosened the fibers by scratching the surface of the husk with one finger of the pincers, then pulling off the strips. The nut itself was opened by inserting one finger of the claw into the soft eye thus disclosed. Both Tom and Yani said they had watched the whole process. They said they had often seen the crabs in the tops of the palms eating young leaves, but that they had never seen a crab actually cut down a nut. The crab, of course, is a general scavenger, not confined to a diet of coconuts.

But of the animals of Ella, the rats made the strongest impression on me. Again on that first day, when we were laying the well line, we stopped as usual to drink a few coconuts, and as usual we cut them open to eat some of the flesh. I happened to go back, a few minutes later, to the place where we had opened the coconuts, to find it teeming with tremendous, fearless rats, avidly disposing of the last traces of flesh in our opened nuts.

The rats, once one started to notice them, were everywhere, in overwhelming numbers. These rats (identified as *Rattus exulans* the Pacific Island rat) are one of the great plagues everywhere in Polynesia and Micronesia. They were present on Falarik and Falalap all right—we kept up a pretty steady rat-trapping operation in our camp at the Fan Nap—but the numbers on Ella were really fantastic.

The Japanese had introduced monitor lizards into Ifaluk to help control the rats. I had wondered how a big, rather awkward lizard would ever be able to achieve much efficiency at rat catching; and I still don't understand the process. But after seeing the rats on Ella, where the monitor lizards had not become established, I was ready to believe that they might be responsible for the relative scarcity of rats on the main islands. These Ella rats were so bold and shameless that I couldn't resist using some film and flash bulbs on them.

Falarik, Falalap, Ella—this still wasn't all the dry land of Ifaluk. There was also the tiny islet of Elangalap. It was an ever present element in our view across the lagoon from the front of the Fan Nap —a dozen coconut palms grouped in the central horizon, breaking the white line of surf that marked the western reef. We looked at this islet, we talked about it, we photographed it, but we never got around to visiting it until we were faced with the problem of locating a well there.

The well on Elangalap, of course, yielded salt water—after all, you could hardly expect much fresh water to accumulate under a pair of mounds of coral sand each about 150 feet long and 75 feet wide. We were able to explore the island in no time at all, when we finally got around to landing on it. It was so small that it seemed easily possible to make a complete list of the plants—twenty-one different kinds. Man quite surely had never bothered with the cultivation of Elangalap, so that these twenty-one plants seemed to represent a sort of basic list of the things that grew naturally on a coral beach in the tropical Pacific. Except that even here, according to Yani, the coconuts had been planted. The flora, then, was composed of plants with some means for over-water dispersal—by wind, by currents, by birds—and they were plants that could withstand salt spray on their leaves and salt water around their roots.

Elangalap could have served as a model for the cartoonist's oceanic islet, as long as you kept your back to the bigger islands across the lagoon; and it had all of the fascination of the miniature. Looking back now, I realize we should have spent much more time there, studying the conditions of existence on this coral fragment. But it was a long row across the lagoon and things were always crying for study on our doorstep. And time, for me at least, was slipping away dizzily.

CHAPTER IX

SHIP COME

WE WERE never able to probe very deeply into the Ifalukian psychology or sex life. We skimmed along on the pleasant surface. I suspect that both of us were seeing, really, what we wanted to see. And often I suspected that the Ifalukians, sensitive people that they were, acted the way they thought we thought they should act. So we were back at the endlessly fascinating business of human relations—of the basic similarity of human nature everywhere, and of the endless diversity of human behavior. This, needless to say, was a frequent topic for those prolonged discussions.

I should note, while on this subject, that the Ifalukians were essentially very modest. The ladies, as I mentioned earlier, were always extremely careful about their skirts, and I never saw the men take off their loin-cloths even when out swimming and fishing in some remote place with other men. This modesty seemed so deeply ingrained that I would think it antedated Western contact—particularly since it was not associated with Western dress, and since it did not involve peculiar Western elements like covering the female breasts.

We found out very little about sex habits on Ifaluk. But everything seemed to indicate the essential correctness of the account included by Burrows and Spiro in their ethnographic study of Ifaluk based on the 1947 visit. Apparently "affairs" were rather free but quite discreet among the young people, leading eventually to a quite settled married life when a man formally moved into the household of his beloved. We came across incidents where men had changed wives later in life, or where married men were said to be straying. But Don guessed that marital fidelity was about the same in Ifaluk as in the United States—whatever that may mean. There remains the puzzle of the absence of illegitimate births among the young unmarried, and of the low birth rate of the married.

There was only one open break in the serenity, kindliness and security of the Ifalukian personality. That was Tarof, the island psychotic. I don't know what variety of insanity afflicted Tarof. He seemed mild enough to us. He was kept shut up in a "cage" about halfway down the Falarik shore, isolated from the other houses. He could escape from his hut readily enough, however, and he would come down to the path sometimes as we went by to give us half-finished woven purses, for which we gave him cigarettes in exchange.

He was said, sometimes, to throw stones at people, and to have threatened his wife. Spiro, from his observation of Tarof in 1947, thought he was in rebellion against the subtle but all-pervasive chiefly authority. Perhaps the surface conformity of Ifaluk, the non-aggressive, non-competitive personality of the people had a cost that we couldn't calculate. But then, every cultural conformity must have its cost; and the apparent charm and peace of the Ifalukian way of life might well be worth the sacrifice of the occasional individual—if that was really entailed.

The charm certainly captured us. I remember feeling it particularly strongly one afternoon late in the summer when we gave a tea party for a group of ladies. It was really a song-recording session. But I remember it as a tea party, even though there was no tea.

Ted had brought along a recording machine. It was really a wind-up, portable dictating machine, made for people who like to dictate notes in the field. It was a poor specimen of a poor variety of instrument for the purpose of making records of voices. But it was all we had.

Ted had managed to live an easier and less-harried life by maintaining that he was completely unmechanical. At least that's my explanation of his pose. Whatever the explanation, the fact was that he remained helpless before any gadget, with the result that someone always came forward to fix it or run it for him. This was true in the case of the recording machine. He had it, wanted to use it, and yet remained completely baffled by its workings. So I took over as sound engineer. (The very poor results, of course, are to be blamed entirely on the machine.)

On this particular afternoon Ted had several men and women from whom he wanted to get song recordings. There was an intermittent rain, so we set everything up in a chummy fashion in the kitchen area of the Fan Nap.

Presently Ted asked for some love songs from the women. For that, the men had to go out of hearing, to observe the proprieties, and they never came back. So it became a hen party except for Ted and me (we apparently didn't count as males on Ifaluk). I got into a routine of playing back about ten revolutions of the turntable, which didn't take up much time, and yet gave them an idea of what was being recorded. When one lady was through, I simply held up the mike and asked, "Who's next?" Someone would step up and take over. They even got the idea of giving a brief preliminary announcement of what they were going to sing—at least I suppose that is what they were doing when they talked into the mike first.

After a while we got to the end of the tape—200 feet of it. But the ladies showed no signs of going home. I began to feel uneasy—the same unease I remember when I have found myself trapped by the Ladies Auxiliary of something or other with a promise to give a talk on South American gardens. An informal talk, however, was clearly not expected this time. It occurred to me that we should serve tea. This didn't seem practical. Then I remembered the great pile of tins of cookies, included in our supplies because Bob Rofen was alleged to have a sweet tooth. Surely, he wouldn't need all of those cookies.

I relayed the suggestion to Ted and Don who had been lurking just inside all this time. The cookies were passed around and munched with evident pleasure. One old woman had a little trouble because of her lack of teeth, as she demonstrated in an unembarrassed way. She solved the problem by breaking the cookies into crumbs before eating.

Chatter flowed around me all during the consumption of the cookies. I grinned, and tried to look at ease. Presently, however, it was clear that they were asking for something—looking directly at me and saying "Pipi, pipi." This I had learned meant pictures—the photographs of our wives and children that we had brought with us. Everyone on the island must have seen these photographs several times, but they seemed to get an endless pleasure out of looking at them and speculating about the characteristics of our families.

This turned out to be a little different, though. They started to sing to the pictures, the sort of song, I judge, that one sings about some close friend, relative or lover who is away. "How I wish you were here" sort of songs. They did this for each picture, one by one. Then, with many expressions of thanks, they got up and went home. We felt that the recording session, as a tea party, had been a great success. We seemed to be firmly established with the ladies—on a strictly motherly or sisterly basis.

The end, for me, was closing in. My eye was caught, one evening, by the label on the binder in which I was filing my notes. The label read "Zoology 38." Lectures. Committee meetings; neckties; shoes; decisions; grades and student conferences. All the dread paraphernalia of the so-called civilized world. Why can't we have all of this and heaven too—the comforts of our culture and the comforts of Ifaluk— keep medicine, art, science and leave winter and its clothing and all of the nasty complexities of organization. We can't, of course, if only because of size. So I shoved it all out of my mind; more than a week remained and I resolved to live in that present.

We were due to be picked up on September 12th. On the afternoon of September 4th, as we were working away on the specimens that had been collected during the morning, we were stopped by the cry of "sail-o" spreading over the island. I went into a complete funk. They were cheating, coming to pick us up ahead of time. I could hardly bring myself to go down to the shore to see what manner of ship it was.

The ship turned out to be a destroyer on a routine mission through the islands, but I wasn't completely reassured until I heard this from the ship's officers themselves when they came ashore. Don, with two months still ahead of him, was able to look at the whole thing more blithely and he and Yani paddled out to greet the ship in Yani's tiny canoe. They were stuffed with ice cream, milk, cake and all that sort of thing in the CPO mess, and were twice swamped by squalls on the way back home. They finally got back with a load of damp cigarettes and soaked magazines.

It was a vivid reminder of the inevitable end—though I do remember clinging to a faint hope that the outside world might forget us. We couldn't bank on that, though, so Ted and I tried to get all of the loose ends of our activities tucked away. We went over the census, household by household, to be sure everything was straight. Ted worked away packing up his ethnographic things—adzes, model canoes, weavings and the like. We went over the notes on the uses of the different plants with Tom and the chiefs. I did some frantic insect collecting and Don and I made a noble effort to clean up on the lizards. The lizards made fools of us with no trouble at all—but the kids of Ifaluk collected them later, after I had left, easily, after the time-honored way of kids with lizards.

We were sad at the thought of leaving Ifaluk; and it became apparent that the people of Ifaluk were sad at the thought that Ted and I were going to go away. They gave us parties, they brought us presents, they kept counting how many days were left and asking when would we come back.

The young men of the island gave us a party. They worried about this for days. It was to be a highly selective party, with only the young blades who had worked most closely with us—no stodgy elders or chiefly personages. They had found out that we liked the fermented coconut sap, the toddy that they called "tubwa" on Ifaluk. Fermentation on Ifaluk was prohibited by the chiefs to avoid the strife that might come with drunken habits. Yani tried, by indirection, to find out whether the chiefs would be bothered if we were served tubwa at this party, and he got an indirect permission to go ahead. They accumulated lobsters and coconut crabs and such-like goodies. It was really to be a feast.

And it was. It was held in the schoolhouse yard, and only the invited guests came—I had thought that any restriction of guest list would be impossible on communal Ifaluk. The tubwa spread a warm feeling of good fellowship through everyone. I really liked the stuff—it had a very pleasant, sour tang, reminiscent of good cider. In this soft, moon-drenched atmosphere, reality lost all its hard corners, and every man became a brother and the world a paradise.

Then, on the last night, the chiefs gave us a party. And to this the whole island came. And we drank tubwa with them! We were all very gay, because we liked each other so much; and very sad because we would have to part so soon.

I was awakened about 2 A.M. by Tawelimal's soft voice calling from outside—"Marston, Marston, ship come!"

I pulled myself out of bed and wandered down to the shore. There, across the lagoon, were the lights of the ship anchored outside the reef. The West had turned up on schedule to claim us.

2

SEPTEMBER TO NOVEMBER

By Donald P. Abbott

CHAPTER X

AN END AND A BEGINNING

OUTSIDE the rain came down in driving, drenching sheets. Water spilled in flickering streams from the thatched corners of the house and from the swaying coconut leaves. Rivers sluiced down the nearby coconut trunks to end with a monotonous drumming in the iron rainbarrels. Even the air inside was wet. I glanced out the back of the Fan Nap, between the little altar and the gasoline stove. Soumat house was barely visible through the downpour. Nearly three inches of rain in the last few hours, and no sign yet of any letup. The Coleman lantern beside me burned steadily with a soft and soothing hiss.

I sat at Marston's old work table, now mine, and stared at a sheet of white paper in the typewriter. It was headed "Abbates Journal, Sept. 13, 1953." The rest was blank. And it wasn't September 13th at all, but September 18th. The blank represented . . . just five days? It seemed a lot longer. I looked back at the last, short entry by Marston Bates.

"And so the ship came," it said, only that and nothing more; no transition, no flippant quips, no encouraging words to the permanent party, no good-byes. The words brought back vivid recollections of that day.

The Trust Territory ship METOMKIN had come on time, and lay off Ella islet. Through the binoculars I could see the launch swinging over the side and starting toward the ship pass. I walked from the beach to the Fan Nap. Ted and Marston were there, Ted busily pack-

125

ing some last minute things. Marston sat quietly on an old carton of
C-rations, staring at the ragged coconut mats that were the floor. He
didn't look at the ship and he didn't want to talk to anyone. I went
back to the beach.

The launch moved across the still lagoon, leaving a thin, spreading
wake. Now we could make out figures waving. A good section of the
Ifaluk population began to collect, the younger men along the shore
and the older ones on the shaded grass in front of the Fan Nap.

The launch cut a sharp arc toward the east, slowed to a crawl and
came straight in through a gap in the patch reefs just south of the
little copra shed. It beached gently, and the West was here.

The launch crewmen were dark-skinned fellows from Palau, and
beside them the newcomers seemed strangely pale. Josh Tracey, the
tall and bony geologist from the Geological Survey team on Guam,
swung down with a splash and waded ashore grinning. Then Ted
Arnow, the Trust Territory hydrologist, with his shock of stiff, dark
hair and the beginnings of a mustache. Frederick (Ted) Bayer, wiry
invertebrate zoologist from the Smithsonian Institution was next. And
then Bob Rofen, ichthyologist from the George Vanderbilt Foundation, complete with elephant hat and brightly colored aloha shirt. We
shook hands all around, unloaded the launch, and walked over to the
Fan Nap to pay respects to the chiefs and others.

The introductions made it immediately apparent that we had a
confusing surplus of "Teds." Ted Burrows would be leaving, but that
still left us with two. Ted Arnow settled the matter by introducing
himself as "Arnow."

The METOMKIN spent nearly half the day off Ella. The copra
buyer from Yap was aboard, and the launch went busily back and
forth carrying copra bags and Ifalukians. The copra, over nine tons
of it, had been sitting around for months and the people were afraid
it might not be in good shape, but it brought a standard price of
$80.00 a ton. Between copra sales and our payments for well digging
and general help, Ifaluk was fairly well-heeled and anxious to get a
variety of trade goods. It was a disappointment to find that the ship
had little beyond cigarettes, matches, and kerosene to sell this trip.
No good knives, no adze blades, no red cloth, no face paint, no dyes,

no mosquito nets, and no rice or canned meat. We were running low on cigarettes ourselves, since we had been supplying smokes for quite a section of the population off and on, so I laid in a new supply.

Then it was time for the ship to leave. Goodbyes were as falsely hearty as they usually are, and the launch eased out from shore between the reefs and picked up speed. The passengers stood. Ted Burrows, solid and stocky and brown; with his horn-rimmed glasses and full grey beard he looked every inch the senior anthropologist in the tropics. Marston, gaunt and brown, dressed in shorts, wreath and shell necklace, could have passed as a weary Micronesian. The white wake carved the quiet blue and in a minute the boat was a toy in the distance. We turned and left the beach.

It was an end that wasn't an end, and a beginning that wasn't a beginning. For a brief moment, when the launch stood ready for the last trip out, I had wanted badly to leave with it. At the same time I would not have left the island for anything. This visit of the METOM-KIN had been a sharp reminder that my real ties were with the outer world, not Ifaluk. This had always been clear at the intellectual level, but not always so at the emotional level. At times those outer ties had seemed the slenderest of threads, spun over an infinite gulf in space and time. It is not easy to understand or to express the degree to which our thoughts and feelings had embraced the atoll and its folk. Though not of the island, we had come to feel a part of it until it seemed a home more real than those we had left so far behind.

The visits of other ships had had very little effect on our atoll lives. This one had taken away fast friends and left relative strangers. And it had brought the first mail from home. The letters were in my back pocket. It was a comfort just to have them there, but somehow I could not bring myself to open and read them just yet.

Hard physical work is a fine distraction at a time like this, and there was a lot of it to do. A mound of new supplies lay on the beach; gasoline in drums, extra food, flit guns, drinkables to replenish our depleted supply, and a pile of tools and personal gear. The newcomers were bursting with enthusiasm and western energy, and we had lots of help getting things to the Fan Nap.

It was quite clear that the main house wouldn't hold all of us for sleeping and working. With chiefly permission we set up a new tent on the site of the old office tent-fly, and Bayer and Rofen moved in their gear and bunks. In the Fan Nap I took over Marston's old work table, and things were shifted to make more convenient sleeping and working space for Josh and Arnow. We made a start on the things in the supply tent and in no time it was evening.

The supper was good, the evening drinks and conversation better. Afterward I settled among my notebooks with the letters from home, opening them carefully in chronological order and savoring them slowly. They were the sort of letters a husband far from home longs to get. Rich and warm, personal as a soft caress, full of news and love and the message that things at home were in competent hands. There were pictures of the baby playing in the yard, and there were no portents of impending trouble or futile appeals to come home now. I read them all twice. It took a long time, and afterward I slipped into bed feeling once again a whole man.

We started to work early the next morning. The supply tent was turned inside out, and all sorts of gear that hadn't been used during the first half of the expedition was hauled out into daylight and unpacked. Things seemed to have survived storage well, and a good portion of Rauau village gathered to watch and help as needed.

Among other things to come out was the big crate with the rubber boat, a heavy black six-man Navy rubber assault raft. We unrolled it on the lawn and attached the hand pump. Everyone was greatly impressed when it was blown up for the first time. Then came the outboard motors. We had brought three of these, apparently on the theory that sheer numbers ought to guarantee a workable motor. One of the boxes was already open, and Bob Rofen started on this one.

Seeing the thing set up on the rim of an oil drum recalled an old argument with Marston over this very piece of equipment. The roots of the argument, like those in many another we had, were curiously confused. Marston had long espoused the view that the real tools of a naturalist are brain and eyes, to be supplemented by pencil, notebook, and handlens as required. He had compromised this purist conception to the extent of bringing along as well some butterfly nets, insect pins, thermometers, and several cameras, but his arguments had been so

ABOVE The Satawal canoes were made ready for the next lap of their ocean voyage.

BELOW For "rop" fishing, lengths of rope were wound spirally with strips of palm leaves, giving the effect of monstrous green tinsel.

In "yating" fishing, great lengths of seine were carried down to the canoes and then played out in the lagoon to form a huge semicircle, which was slowly closed until the fish that did not try to leap free were funnelled into wicker traps.

LEFT The cordage of Ifaluk was made from the fiber of coconut husks; the husks were first soaked in fresh water until soft, and the fibers then cleaned in the lagoon.

BELOW The men carried bundles of coconut fiber about with them and, in moments of relaxation, made rope—like women knitting in our culture.

persuasive that I had taken a long step in the direction of his concept.

Then, in the middle of the first session, he had about-faced and insisted on opening an outboard motor. At the time this seemed a traitorous piece of philosophical backsliding. What was worse, I had enjoyed our quiet trips across the lagoon, and I had a sudden vision of the tranquility of Ifaluk shattered by the roar of motors.

Marston refused to discuss the matter at the level of principle. He felt sure the noise would be confined to a gentlemanly puttering. He recalled pleasant days exploring tributaries of the upper Orinoco in Colombia with skiff and outboard. He spread a glowing vision of ourselves reclining in the BWUP while the marvels of western engineering drove us swiftly over the billows. My arguments dropped to the practical level of "Will the damned thing be worth the trouble?," and petered out.

The matter settled itself, a fine lesson in the futility of words. Unpacked and set up, the motor had stubbornly refused to run. Without a word we returned it to its case.

Bob Rofen and Ted Bayer were made of sterner stuff, and for the present work motors were definitely needed. As Josh and Arnow loaded themselves for inspection and sampling of the line of wells at the northern end of Falarik, the motors were uncrated and looked over. It was an occasion for profanity; two of the motors were in unusably bad shape, and the third needed cleaning and lacked a tool kit and spare parts. The two men set to work, and soon the best motor was spread in parts on a large tarp on the lawn. Painstakingly it was cleaned and reassembled with only slight interruptions in the form of intermittent showers. The young blades of Ifaluk, and some of the older ones like Maroligar and the craftsman Gavileisei, formed an interested circle of observers.

Put together again the motor was loaded with gas and oil, and Bob and Ted took turns spinning it with the starter cord. When they were tired the men of Ifaluk took over, and during the next couple of days nearly every male between the ages of twelve and fifty stopped by the Fan Nap to give the thing a ritual whirl or two, even the portly chief Wolpaitik and Arueligar the medicine-man. Laughter and excitement were gradually replaced by patience and finally boredom as the motor refused to work. Slowly the circle of admirers declined to a diehard core of younger men. At last, on the third day, the motor choked, gasped, and went into a spluttering run. There was a ragged cheer and the crowd of spectators was immediately swelled by a group of men who had been taking their ease in the shade of nearby Rolong canoe house. Someone jiggered the gas lever and the motor peacefully declined and died again, but the worst was over.

Then the rains came in earnest, pouring rains that kept us indoors for hours at a stretch. It had been a wet week for the newcomers anyway, with nearly an inch of rain a day, but this hadn't really interfered with settling down and getting field work underway. Josh and Ted Arnow, working together, had managed to check on all the wells in north and central Falarik, sampling water and looking at soil profiles. Yani and I had taken a last vegetation profile, and had completed an interrogation of Maroligar, Toroman and others on Ifalukian uses of various land plants. Bob and Ted Bayer and their helpers had at last put a motor into action. And in the housekeeping we were down to a routine again. The heavy rains came at a good time, for together with the evenings in the Fan Nap, they gave us a chance to catch up on organizing notes and to sit down and plan our work together.

Idealistically, we had hoped to outline all the basic objectives and procedures in advance through joint discussion. This hadn't worked to perfection. For one thing we had never all been able to get together at one time. For another, detailed plans have to be made on the spot, and require more or less continual revision as work goes on. But in our earlier meetings, held in the conference rooms, restaurants, and bars of St. Louis, Washington, and Guam, we had settled on a two-fold general purpose for the expedition, beyond the overall directive of the Pacific Science Board to "investigate the atoll." The first, as Marston has pointed out, was to study the natural history of Micronesian man in his natural habitat. The second was to survey the atoll environment—to get an overall view of its form and physical conditions, its fauna and flora, and something of the interrelations of these things with each other and with man.

Not that we expected anything like a complete picture. Even if this were possible it was a task for an army of workers with unlimited funds and time, and the result would probably have been a mountain of information beyond human ability to digest. What we wanted was a simplification, probably a very great over-simplification, in which the realities were not too distorted; a rough picture of the anatomy of the atoll, and some conception of its physiology. This seemed better than a detailed study of a few of the island's organs or systems, each portrayed in splendid isolation and detail, though it was clear that some parts would be much better known than others.

More and more we found ourselves in basic agreement as to how different phases of the work might be tied together. For example, Marston and I had made our vegetation profiles along the lines of wells crossing the island, so that water resources, plants, and soil profiles could be taken together. Island trails, houses, and lines of wells made good landmarks for geological observations which could be plotted directly on maps already made during the first half of the work. At the same time, the geological and surveying observations would improve these maps immensely. The land profiles were to be continued seaward and lagoonward, as feasible, for land and reef on an atoll form a natural continuum. Each of us would work these lines for his own specialties.

The result should be, we thought, a series of profiles across the atoll, studied in detail. In the areas between we could make more cursory observations and interpolate. There would be plenty of opportunity for digressions into other regions and time to fulfill individual and more limited objectives.

CHAPTER XI

MOSTLY ABOUT WATER

RIGHT after breakfast Bakal came over to the Fan Nap with a hoarse voice and running nose. A few minutes later Tom showed up with the same symptoms. Then Yani, who reported that his wife felt sick, and that Fagolier was sitting over in Falepenach canoe house sneezing and feeling miserable. I got out the aspirin and nose-drops and asked how come everyone was getting colds. It was the trade ship, Yani answered. Every time it stopped by the island, lots of people came down with colds.

I gave doses of nosedrops and aspirin to everyone and carried the bottles over to Falepenach canoe house; Talimeira, the local western style "doctor" had gone fishing. Yani came along to interpret. It was darkish inside, for the coconut leaf mats that had been put up over the front of the building to keep out the wind and rain had not yet been taken down. We stooped to get under the big side-beams of the house and went inside.

Fagolier sat on a coconut mat with one knee drawn up and an old blanket over his shoulders. Around him clustered some of the worried men and women of his family. As we entered he raised his great head, smiled, greeted me with unintelligible gutturals, and went into a coughing spell. When it was over I took his pulse, which seemed close to normal, and laid a hand on his massive forehead. There was no fever. Yani explained about the nosedrops and aspirin. Fagolier cheerfully agreed to try them, and the medicine went down accompanied by some exaggerated grunts and grimaces that brought laughter from the family audience. The slight tension that had been present immediately relaxed, and it seemed to me this bit of dignified clowning had been deliberately and skillfully done to put everyone at ease. I told Fagolier, through Yani, that he ought to keep warm, try some hot drinks, and generally take things easy. He agreed. Not that taking things easy would be especially difficult for an elderly high-ranking gentleman of Ifaluk, but Fagolier had been working pretty steadily on the unfinished canoe in Falepenach these last few days. The nose-drops were already beginning to clear his head, and I walked back toward the Fan Nap feeling like young Dr. Kildare.

By this time noises were coming from around the benjo down by the lagoon shore. There was more milling about and shouting than might be expected had some occupant merely fallen through the floor. Turning down, I could see that activities centered at the end of the small stone jetty where it jutted beyond the benjo. Here Ted Arnow and Josh were struggling to hold upright a heavy square tube made of four boards nailed together, while several helpers under Maroligar's direction piled blocks of dead coral around its base. At the top of the wooden column was a small platform.

In a few minutes the tube was solidly braced in place. Arnow made a trip to the Fan Nap and returned with one of his portable tide gauges, technically a Stevens type F water-level recorder. He placed the square gray metal case on the platform, and dangled the small float and counterweight on their wire cables down the center of the wooden tube. Then he took the top off and explained the shiny brass works of the instrument. Essentially it consisted of a paper-covered cylinder that was rolled back and forth by the up-and-down movements of the float. Resting lightly on the paper was a writing pen driven by a precision seven-day clock. The idea was to get a graphic record of the tidal changes in sea level. The lagoon near the Fan Nap had seemed a good place to get this, for there were no suitably protected places on the outer reef, and our casual observations had indicated that the lagoon tides pretty well paralleled the tides of the open sea outside. (As it turned out later this wasn't quite correct.) Arnow had a second tide gauge which was to be moved about to record the rise and fall of water in the wells, for on an island like Ifaluk the water level of the fresh-water wells changes somewhat with the tidal cycle in the surrounding sea.

Hydrologic studies get to be pretty complex and technical at times, but the purposes and at least some of the basic ideas are understandable to the non-specialist. All life needs water. Protoplasm itself is mostly water, and living things on land are continually losing their moisture through evaporation from leaves or skin, and from such activities as breathing and excreting. Most familiar organisms replace this loss by eating and drinking, or by absorption through roots or skin. For land forms, and, oddly enough, for some marine forms too, getting enough water to offset the normal loss is often a problem. It's not that the world as a whole has any lack of water. Nearly three-quarters of the globe is covered with it, but most of this is too salty to be used directly by the things that live on land. Arnow's concern, even in his tidal measurements, was not with the sea as such; he was interested in fresh water that was available for human and plant use —water on or in the ground.

On an atoll all the fresh water ultimately comes from rain, present or past. Ifaluk is one of the wetter atolls, getting, Arnow thought, an average of 100–120 inches a year. Not that anyone had ever measured the rainfall here before, but our own records and the longer ones for several other islands in the Carolines give basis for a reasonable guess. During the summer, the wetter part of the year, we averaged about a foot of rainfall a month, the rains seemingly coming whenever we took cameras into the field, or settled ourselves comfortably to make notes in unsheltered areas. Marston and I had discovered quite early that dime-store plastic food bags make light and handy covers for notes and cameras during sudden showers. There is less rain during the winter, but there is really no dry season. And the island shows the results of this. In spite of poor soils in most places, a lush cap of greenery covers Ifaluk from beach to beach.

Some parts of the Carolines get even more rain, but not all atolls are so lucky. Eniwetok in the northern Marshall islands averages some fifty inches a year, and the southern Gilberts get only about thirty-nine, nearly the same as Boston. Actually, these yearly totals are a bit deceptive, for it's not only the amount of rainfall but also its distribution through the year that is important. On drier atolls the rains are more seasonal, and there are seasons and even years of severe drought. Here the vegetation is less dense, with fewer species present. The rich swamps and dense growths of ferns on ground and trees are gone. Coconuts and Pandanus grow, but breadfruit and taro are harder to maintain. The driest atolls are uninhabited by man, and the conditions approach those of a desert. On arid Bikar and Pokak, atolls in the northern Marshalls, the botanist Ray Fosberg found only nine species of higher plants struggling to maintain a foothold. Oceanic man has left such islets to the turtles and crabs, and to the great colonies of seabirds that find a refuge there.

Has Ifaluk ever had a drought? I asked old Toroman one day whether he could remember a time when there was not enough water on Ifaluk. The chief gave me a long blank look. I asked again, this time whether he could remember a season or time when there was little rain. Immediately Toroman shook his head vigorously. "Always rain," he said emphatically, "Always too much rain." He said it in such a disapproving manner that I guessed he thought I was complaining about the recent weather, and he was agreeing with me. But other informants gave the same general response, and it looks as though rainfall is never what an ecologist might call a "limiting factor" here on Ifaluk. Fresh water is scarce only for a period after a typhoon sweeps the sea in waves across the island, salting soils and wells.

The Ifalukians made almost no attempt to catch rainwater directly, though Arnow did note two households besides our own where rain running down the trunks of coconut trees was caught in old oil drums. In one of these, Apilimat family was using the water to nurse along a few small, chlorotic tobacco plants, with results that suggested tobacco would continue in short supply on the island.

Most of the rain that falls on the island sinks into the ground. There is little runoff into the sea or lagoon even during heavy downpours for the stony soil is porous and absorbs water like a giant sponge. Quite a bit of this rainwater later evaporates from soil and plants, for even the sea winds that pass over the atoll are not saturated with moisture, but the water loss here is not excessive compared with the rainfall. The bulk of the falling rain is conserved as soil and ground water.

The deep foundation of the island is ancient reef, extending no one knows how far below the present surface of the atoll. This foundation, like the upper soil, is relatively porous, and the entire base below mean ocean level is permeated by the sea. This being the case one might expect the wells on atolls to be salty, and some of them are. Where rains are light, soils too porous, islets very small, or wells too close to shore, the ground water is too saline for human use.

What keeps the wells on Ifaluk and many other atolls fresh is the abundant rainfall plus the fortunate circumstance that seawater, because of its salts, is slightly heavier than fresh water. The ratio of the weights of the two waters is about 41:40. Fresh and salt water mix readily when stirred together; but if one takes a pan of seawater and carefully adds a glass of fresh at the edge, the latter, being slightly lighter, will tend to float out on the surface of the salt with relatively little mixing.

And this is what happens down below the surface of the islet. Rain soaks into the soil, wets the ground, and trickles down through pebbles and sand till it comes to the subterranean level saturated by the sea. Here the fresh water comes to rest, gradually collecting and forming a great underground pool which actually floats on the underlying seawater. There is mixing where the two layers come together but this is little and slow, for waters in a sand filter or sponge aren't easily stirred, and upward diffusion of salt is slight. As more rain enters, the fresh-water pool enlarges and thickens. It has weight, and since it floats only by displacing an equal weight of salt water, it presses the salty layer down in the middle and out at the sides.

This underground reservoir of fresh water on an island is what hydrologists call a Ghyben-Herzberg lens: Ghyben-Herzberg, after the Dutch and German workers who first wrote of the phenomenon; lens, because the pool is lens-shaped, thickest under the central region of the island (ideally, at least) and thinning down to almost nothing at the shores. The lens tends to be biconvex, with a fat bulge on the lower side and a slight convexity perhaps one-fortieth as great on top.

The water level is highest just where the ground is usually lowest, and in the central taro swamps the top of the lens is often right at the surface. Where the land is higher on either side of the swamps, the pool may be several feet below the surface. In the latter regions the shallow-rooted plants live on the soil moisture, and only the deeper-rooted trees reach down to tap the sunken reservoir. Actually, on Ifaluk Arnow found the center of the lens was displaced slightly toward the lagoon side of the islets, probably he thought, because the boulder substrate of the windward shores was more permeable to the sea than the sands and gravel that bordered the lagoon.

This body of soil and ground water is not a static hoard. It is more like a bank account, with material entering and leaving the system all the time. Water income and expenditure are not always in equilibrium; instead, the balance shrinks in the drier seasons and grows during the rains. The size and dynamics of the balance are prime concerns of the professional hydrologist.

Not only does the lens fluctuate in size with seasons, but daily it shifts its vertical position. The level of the sea rises and falls twice during each complete tidal cycle of about twenty-four hours and fifty minutes. There is a corresponding rise and drop of the subterranean sea surface below the lens, though the shifts are delayed and partially damped out under the islands. As a result, the fresh-water reservoir is correspondingly raised and lowered with the tides. This action is slow and causes little mixing. Some fresh water trickles away from the lens at its edges, especially at low tide. Then one can see tiny rivulets seeping out of the beach just above the low water mark, and the water from these is drinkable. What with rain and such seepage at low tides, the inshore tidepools get pretty diluted at times, and marine organisms here must sometimes tolerate salinities only one-sixth that of the sea.

Our hydrologist, Ted Arnow, was a fine asset to an evening bull session. He had done field work on many islands in the course of his assignment as Trust Territory water expert, and his prowling mind had recorded many details of island life remote from hydrology. Individuals are all unique, but perhaps, like some of the rest of our group, Arnow fell into a general category of "hard-headed romantics," a not uncommon type in the sciences. He enjoyed baiting us all from time to time, though we could usually combat this by raising the subject of dousing. Arnow had the professional hydrologist's fine scorn for water-witching, and of course the irritating thing about it was that dousers had sometimes located water where professional hydrologists had failed.

Water samples from all of the wells on Falarik, taken before the heavy rains, were analyzed. Ted ran a few of the simpler tests on the atoll, and announced that the Ifaluk water was fresher than that served to the public on Guam, where continued heavy use of ground water had seriously depleted the underground lens, and traces of salt water were being pumped in with the fresh. There were traces on Ifaluk too, of course, especially in wells near shore. But in the taro swamps and the centrally located wells on the larger islands, which were sampled in September and again in November, the chloride content generally ran below twenty parts per million, indicating a sea-water contamination of less than one part per thousand of fresh water.

For all the good water supply available on Ifaluk, the local inhabitants didn't use very much of it directly. They drank some and used some in cooking, but they preferred, as we did, the juice and sap of the coconut. People rinsed off in fresh water now and then after a swim, but the real bathtub was the lagoon. Clothes, except for skirts of the women working in the taro swamps, didn't get too dirty, for they were worn into the sea several times each day. Occasionally they would be washed separately in well-water. Several of the wells were reserved for the retting of coconut husks for their fibers. After several months immersion, the ripe coconut husks could be torn apart easily and the fibers cleaned by pounding and washing at the edge of the lagoon. These were twisted into rough strands and a pair of strands then rolled into rope on the thigh—no job for men with hairy legs, we found; hairs are pulled out by the roots in the process. Coconut rope made by rolling or braiding coconut husk fibers was common in Polynesia and Micronesia until recent times. It still serves on Ifaluk in lieu of nails for the building of houses and canoes, and it is from this material that the great fishnets are made. But the greatest value of the good water supply of Ifaluk lies in its effect on the vegetation.

With rains replenishing soil and ground water the atoll is fertile and richly productive of food. Without this water life would be hard indeed, and very likely man would not have settled here.

Quickly the days passed. Josh Tracey and Ted Arnow were scheduled to be picked up on the return trip of the METOMKIN on September 26th, giving them little over a week to finish their field work. Well-sampling had been carried out first, so Arnow would be free to help Josh with other aspects of the geological and topographical survey. The rest of us helped them as we were needed, and as our own studies of the marine environment allowed.

The next step in the geological work was surveying, for we all felt the need of a contour map of Falarik islet. Josh lugged out the alidade, set it up in front of the Fan Nap, and cast his eye around for a likely benchmark. After some discussion he chiseled an "X" on a massive and permanent-looking slab of blackened coral at the base of a coconut tree just southwest of the Fan Nap, and the surveying was on.

Helping Josh and Arnow in the surveying was a pair of young men, Talimeira and Sagolimar, both in the twenties from the looks of them. Talimeira had a quick mind and knew some English, which made him a useful collaborator. He spoke Japanese as well, and was able to write it, for as a child he had been sent to a Japanese school on Yap. He had served as a sort of chore-boy for Burrows and Spiro on their earlier trip to Ifaluk, and had spent some months in the Palau islands after the war, going to an American school and getting some training as a medical technician. This latter amounted to something less than that received by a Navy corpsman, but by Ifaluk standards Talimeira was a doctor of western medicine. Talim's wife was a lovely girl, hardly sixteen to judge from appearances, and as yet with no children. The other surveying assistant, Sagolimar, spoke only a few words of English and perhaps for this reason seemed less intelligent, though he was always friendly and cooperative. He had married a cheerful widow with a wandering eye, who seemed years older than himself.

Surveying operations proceeded rapidly and the team became a familiar sight, Josh peering through the telescope and waving his hands in the time-honored manner of surveyors while Talim and

Sagol took turns handling the surveying rod. In no time, it seemed, the coastal survey line was carried around the island, and when contours were added to the base map it had a most professional look. Not that contours were much of a problem; the highest point on Falarik turned out to be only a bit over fifteen feet above mean sea level. Mean sea level itself was established pretty accurately later, on the basis of Arnow's tidal records.

Some interesting things showed up in the course of this work. For one thing, it was clear that the north end of Falarik had been a separate island until relatively recent times. The old channel between the north tip and the rest of Falarik was somewhat lower than the ground on either side, and its two ends were well-marked; the inner by a bulge in the contour of the lagoon shore, the outer by a conspicuous dent in the windward coast. Tom pointed out that coconuts grew in the low strip of sandy ground, but that breadfruit trees grew only on the higher banks of brown soil on either side. He told Josh and Arnow that the coconuts had been planted a few years after the big typhoon of 1907, and that when he was a boy the channel was filled with water.

Josh went off to have a talk with Toroman, taking Yani along as interpreter. Sure enough, the old chief remembered that Falarik's north end had been a separate island in his youth. The channel separating this from Falarik had been relatively narrow even then, and apparently a continuous influx of sand from the windward side had gradually plugged it. A few severe storms, notably that of 1907, had completed the union.

This finding explained several things. Among others, it answered a question to which Yani had never been able to reply; why did the main trail along the lagoon shore—Marston's "El Camino Falarik"—end abruptly in the middle of nowhere some distance north of Falarik village, instead of continuing to the north tip of the present islet? Not that there had to be an answer that would seem logical to the western mind, but we had been curious. A new look at the area showed that the big trail ended just at the southern margin of the old channel. Yani and I made a vegetation survey across the island in the old channel bed. The soil here was certainly sandier than that on either side, and all along its course the plants in the old channel were a curious mixture of strand and forest species. Toroman said the old islet had been called Maia, and he sounded the terminal "a" so softly it might almost have been Mai.

The curious outline of the northern quarter of Falarik island was now explained. Not only that, but at last some light was thrown on an old historical problem of islet numbers and names. The explorer Lütke 125 years before had stopped briefly at Ifaluk. His crude sketch map showed the north tip of present Falarik as a separate island. He labelled it "Fararyk," called the remainder of Falarik "Ifalouk," and used the name "Moay" for what is clearly Falalap. Some have since considered that the name "Moay" must refer to tiny Elangalap, but Lütke does not show that island at all, and indeed it is quite possible that this was not formed until later, perhaps partly or largely through the typhoon of 1907. Sarfert, a German visiting the island in 1909, was the first to report the presence of Elangalap, and his description of the islets and use of islet names coincides with the geography and nomenclature of today.

Sarfert, however, considered Lütke's map of the atoll in serious error. He pointed out that there was no separate islet north of Falarik, that Lütke had the island names all mixed up, and that there was no islet at all named Moay. Later, in another connection, he wrote that in the storm of 1907, a small sandbank called Maje had been joined to northern Falarik.

These separate pieces seemed to fit together. Lütke's original map was basically correct though the names he gave for the islets were either confused, or (less likely) underwent a change in usage during the following century. Sarfert was correct in his mention of the union of Maje with Falarik, but wrong in calling the former a small sandbank, and quite in error in his evaluation of Lütke's outline of the islands.

Ifaluk has no written language, and there is no single "correct" spelling for Ifalukian place names. Moay, Maje, and Maia are very probably the same name, spoken by different men in different generations, and falling on different western ears. Allowing the likelihood that Lütke had misapplied his island names, it looked as though we had rediscovered the island of Moay at last.

The low tides had been getting lower as the days went by, and now the tide tables predicted a series that should be especially favorable for marine work. Josh and Ted had not finished their projects on land, but for a period they joined the rest of us on the reefs. Reefs after all are as much a matter for the geologist as for the biologist, and Josh, with extensive experience in the Marshall islands and on Guam, was particularly interested. For the next two days we worked the windward reefs of Falarik, across the islet from home. Bob collected fishes with his helpers; Ted Bayer and I, with Yani, sampled fauna and flora along the reef profile extending outward from the Fan Ni Wa trail; and Josh tramped about with geology pick, canvas sacks, and notebook, breaking off specimens here and there and examining the reef topography. It was cold on the reef flat, but the wind and fine drizzle blowing in from the southwest were partly cut off by the islet at our backs. We worked steadily and waited for a break in the weather that would make a trip to Ella and Elangalap islets worthwhile.

The break didn't come. After breakfast on the third day we walked down from the Fan Nap to stare across the lagoon. It was windy, with a few whitecaps on the water. The sky was a curdled gray but the cloud cover showed signs of breaking on the western horizon. The breakers on the far reef looked uncomfortably large, but it was impossible to judge very well from this distance. We decided to try it. Equipment was quickly packed in the two boats and we pushed off. Josh, Arnow, Yani, Talimeira, and myself took that sturdy scow the BWUP, while Bob and Ted, with Bakal, Tachim, and Tewas manned the rubber assault boat. We decided not to fool with an unreliable outboard, and it was paddles and oars that took us across.

We started at a characteristically Ifalukian pace, neither hurrying nor dawdling. It soon became apparent, however, that Bob in the assault raft was encouraging his companions to beat the BWUP over to Elangalap. The competitive spirit is pretty deeply ingrained in Americans, and we rose to the bait. Yani and Talim seemed to catch a trace of it too, or at least they cooperated with our efforts in a polite way. The rubber boat was slightly faster but the wind kept pushing it off-course toward the north, and we managed to stay about even.

Halfway across someone suggested that we ought to have a name for the rubber raft, a good Ifalukian name like BWUP. There were a few proposals, none of them much good. Then Talim leaned over and murmured something to Yani in a voice too low to catch. Yani promptly burst with laughter. "Wat! Wat!," he said. Shipping his paddle he spread his arms and puffed up his chest hugely. After that he hardly needed to explain that Wat was a sort of family name given to the local puffer fishes (Tetradontids), which inflated themselves like balloons when disturbed. It was a perfect name. No one on Ifaluk who had watched the rubber raft being inflated and slowly taking shape could possibly mistake the connection. Talimeira was modest but very obviously pleased that his suggestion had been received as a stroke of genius. We shouted the name across to the WAT where it was received with similar laughter. The name stuck.

We shipped oars and paddles and tied up to a coral head in the shallows near the inner beach of Elangalap. Josh and Arnow headed for the single well on this speck of an islet, while the rest of us went on to the reef just outside. The tide was moderately low, but with the wind kicking up there were sizeable breakers coming in. The reef was narrow here. Boulders lay scattered in a dense pattern below the beach. Beyond them, the outer reef flat was bare of rocks and planed smooth by the action of the waves, but the fauna and flora were typical of the zone. According to the aerial photographs the seaward margin of the reef dropped off rather steeply. We had hoped to get a better look at this today, but the surf made it impossible even to approach the edge.

Yani and Bakal and the other local men had been sidetracked by a confusion of turtle tracks on the beach. This meant eggs somewhere in the vicinity, and they probed with sticks in likely patches of disturbed sand till the cache was located. There were nearly sixty eggs buried in the hole, not quite fresh, Yani said, but still good to eat. Bakal loaded the eggs into a canvas bucket and brought them along.

Josh and Arnow had completed their observations in another hour.

The rest of us came in and stopped for a look at the well before we left. As everyone had suspected, the water in the well was quite salty. Arnow's analysis later showed it to be nearly half seawater, and a sample taken again in November was nearly 80% as salty as the sea. Certainly well-water from here would be unpotable except perhaps fleetingly after a very heavy rain.

We took to the boats again, and paddled in the direction of Ella islet. The course took us over shallow sandy bottom, and we skirted along the lagoon margin of the western reef. At the edge is the zone of blue coral, perhaps the loveliest of the submarine regions of the atoll. There wasn't time for an extensive look, but we stopped here and there along the way, collecting a few things and noting particular points for more detailed investigations later.

The boats were beached on the lagoon shore of Ella, close to the western tip of the islet. We walked around to the outer shore hugging the beach, for on this part of Ella the vegetation is thick and nearly impassable. Near the tip of the islet and partly buried in the sand was the rusted hulk of an old buoy, a wanderer at rest at last in this unlikely spot.

The southern shore of Ella is a rugged stretch of coast. Here, too, the reef flat is narrow, and the outer ridge feebly developed. When the wind comes in from the south or southwest the waves crest and break in places at the very edges of the islet. Sand straggles in patches from place to place, but along much of the coast the beach is strewn with rugged boulders of pitted reef material tossed ashore like pebbles by the angry waves. The winds of the morning had gradually stilled to a gentle breeze but the sea was still choppy. We worked along the slim reef flat not far from shore. The outermost rampart of the land vegetation here is the Haingei, *Pemphis acidula,* a tough wiry tree with unbelievably hard and heavy close-grained wood. Cutting a branch of it will literally murder the edge of a machete, and, fresh or dry, the wood sinks like stone in the water. The roots creep down the shore and out to sea, coiling their naked red-brown tendrils among the boulders on the reef flat. In the most exposed places, barnacles form a sparse pattern of white low on the tree trunks.

Next on the program was a look at the little salty lake near the western end of the islet. We turned in from shore and forced our way through a narrow opening in the *Pemphis* forest, Bakal and Tachim in the lead. The lake was only a few dozen yards in at this point, and soon we could see it ahead.

It was a lovely little pond, a narrow crystal ovoid perhaps a hundred paces long. Even as we looked the sun came out, pouring down its warmth and light again. Within the barrier of grey-green *Pemphis* trees there was a stillness and peace somehow remote from the restless sea outside. The water level of the lake had dropped a few inches with the tide, exposing dark algae-covered rocks along the sides. A few small fishes skittered away from the water's edge as we approached. Arnow unslung his pack and got out the water sample bottles while the rest of us looked about and began turning over rocks near the rim of the lake.

Ted took his samples and then tasted the water; he always tasted water he was sampling. He spat several times and said, quite unnecessarily, "Salty." We all trusted Arnow's taste buds. I had even tried the water before, on an earlier trip to the lake with Marston. Still, such a remark can be like a wet-paint sign. I tasted the water, and it was salty all right. The later analysis showed it to be about half the salinity of the sea. The plants and animals along the shores of the pool were that curious mixture of marine and freshwater types that one frequently finds in an estuary. Marine algae sat almost side by side with mosses; marine worms and snails huddled together with freshwater insect larvae; pond algae floated in clumps here and there on the surface of the brackish water.

It was time for lunch. We sat down near the shore for a meal of green coconuts, ripe coconuts, sprouted coconuts, and frankfurters. And turtle eggs. Yani and Talimeira had lagged behind us again, and found a second cache of eggs near the western tip of Ella, high in the sand. Like the first batch they weren't exactly fresh, but quite edible. Tachim split several of them, separated yolks from whites, and Tewas cooked the yellow centers in the frankfurter cans over a small fire. They were rather good. Marston would have enjoyed them, I thought, even after his disheartening bout with turtle eggs earlier in the summer.

After lunch we tramped the reefs again, and finally surveyed the line of wells on Ella. There were only three, all deep pits dug along a trail that had been hacked out to make travel easier for the diggers. Arnow took his samples and tasted them. The results were not at all what we had expected. The two wells near the outer and inner shores of Ella, which everyone had expected to be brackish, turned out to be quite drinkably fresh. But in the well at the center of the islet (which theory said should be the freshest of all) the water was detectably salty. Something, perhaps a structural fault of some sort, was disrupting the freshwater lens under the island.

We got back to the Fan Nap for dinner. In the evening Maroligar invited us over to his house for some tubwa and a bit of singing. We came and sat in the cool darkness near the high peaked front of the house and drank. Maroligar sang first. In his low-pitched voice he sang an old chant that he said was a song for the chiefs, and another song for a man going away to a distant island. It was the music of the very far away and long ago. In their monotonous simplicity the chants were scarcely an approach to the simplest of our folk tunes, yet I had heard the type of song so often now that they almost seemed my own. Maroligar's voice was not the best, but there was a sadness in the chants, and a power and a beauty that haunt me yet.

When it was our turn we tried some of the few we all knew. They were things like "Daisy, Daisy," and "I've been working on the railroad." Josh turned out to have quite the decentest voice among us, a suitable successor to Ted Burrows in this respect. But after Maroligar's recital ours was not a very impressive showing. Future anthropologists and other visitors might make a note to bring a song book.

CHAPTER XII

LAGOON INTERLUDES

THE DAY was pleasantly hot. Yani pulled the BWUP over to the nearest patch reef and I dropped the sounding lead on it for a light anchor. We had been taking depths and sketching contours of the lagoon bottom near home, part of checking an hypothesis that might explain the distribution of patch reefs and beds of turtle grass in this region. The work was easy but somewhat tedious, and it called for an occasional break. We lit cigarettes and leaned back, staring lazily over the water.

"Don?" Yani blew a puff of smoke toward Elangalap islet on the far side of the lagoon and followed this with an economical jerk of his head. "Will you swim across to Elangalap?"

Meaning would I dare, of course. He knew I could do it.

"No. You?"

He shook his head. "Me either. I afraid some big fishes." A pause. "Maybe Tarof swim across." He laughed. Tarof was the island psychotic.

Some words have a touch of magic. "Lagoon" is one of these. In many a mind it conjures visions of Dorothy Lamour in a sarong, and brings to the conscious level the travelogue clichés of drowsing palms and dusky maidens. It triggers a romantic itching to get away from it all, that works in much the same way on scientists and tired businessmen. For all its soft Indopacific flavor, lagoon is no oceanic word. Lacuna, its deceased linguistic ancestor, meant lake to the Romans, and in many ways an atoll lagoon is a reef-locked ocean lake.

147

Work in this marine lake went on sporadically all summer. It started almost with the day Ted Burrows, Marston, and I moved into the Fan Nap, and it continued to the end. We found that periodic observations of some things could be tied in nicely with a late afternoon swim. And a sunny day in the lagoon sometimes provided a needed break in other work—especially during the earlier studies of vegetation, food, and the natural history of man. Slowly information on the lagoon accumulated and insights broadened, partly through deliberate effort, partly through more casual observation and rumination.

With the arrival of the second team we had planned a shift in emphasis toward things marine. Work on land continued, of course, but mostly in the fields of hydrology and geology. For the rest it was more a matter of tying up loose ends and filling some of the more conspicuous gaps in earlier projects. Many gaps would never be filled, at least by us; an ecological survey is never really "completed," it is only done.

During the low tides we always took to the outer reefs, for it was impossible to do much there at other times with the surf rolling in. The lagoon, on the other hand, could be worked when the water was high, since studies here involved underwater collecting and observing anyway. But we needed a reasonably calm day. Wind stirs the lagoon and fine sediments rise to cloud the water, limiting vision below the surface to a yard or two.

Lagoon work formed a series of interludes that were many and seldom prolonged. Fragments of work done in fragments of time do not form a narrative, but cut and spliced they make a sequence of sorts. Perhaps from this there emerges a portrait, if not an analysis, of the lagoon.

The Ifaluk lagoon is shaped like a soup-bowl with a flaring rim. The rim is the lagoon shelf, a sandy bottom that slopes gently down from the island beaches and from the inner margin of the western reef. Here in the protected shallows life and color are spread in a rich tapestry. The white of the beach gives way first to the shore-bound green of the turtle grass beds, then to the pastel blue of sea over white sand. Farther out are other greens and blues that mingle in a palette of nameless shades, grading to deep turquoise on the outer shelf. Mottling the whole are the brown shadows of patch reefs on the sand.

Beyond the sandy shelf which forms its rim, the real lagoon begins. The bottom drops off in a steep slope to the main lagoon floor, ten fathoms down. Above this slope the waters darken abruptly, and the central bowl is the blue of cobalt and lapis-lazuli. Looking over the lagoon on a still, bright day one comes to understand why Ifaluk has but a single word for most of the shades of blue and green.

The line separating the turquoise of the shelf from the deep blue of the basin is a barrier of sorts, one that divides the lagoon into two regions, for two different kinds of human activity. This line is strikingly sharp when seen from the shore. From a boat it is less impressive. But seen from under water, on the western side of the lagoon, it is unforgettable . . .

It was a clean crystal afternoon. The WAT had swung gently on its mooring line for hours while a group of us collected in the blue coral region at the inner edges of the western reef. Weary and with buckets loaded we were ready to head for home. Yani and I swam slowly out over the sandy shelf while the loaded WAT trailed idly behind.

The bottom here is coarse clean sand, here bare and there dotted with patches of the stiff green seaweed *Halimeda* whose limy blades litter much of the lagoon floor. We poked casually about isolated lumps of dead coral, their creviced interiors seething with little black and white striped convict fishes. Nearby on the sand Yani picked up a large cone shell, its yellow surface marked with a thousand small brown exclamation points. On the left a big brown coelenterate extended its branched colony like a flexible pine tree from the sandy floor. A touch and it pulled down into its hole, leaving a stinging tentacle across an open coral cut in my hand.

We drifted farther out along the shelf, carried by the current of the rising tide sweeping in across the open reef. Now the waters were about ten feet deep and for a moment more the sandy floor seemed to stretch endlessly ahead. Then, as we skimmed the bottom, the waters darkened before us, and abruptly we were at the edge of the shelf. For a moment it seemed the edge of the world.

My reflex was that of a runner on land, startled by a yawning chasm a step ahead. I stopped suddenly and grabbed for the bottom, and immediately felt foolish for carrying such instincts into an environment where man falls up instead of down.

We swam slowly back and forth over the edge. At the lip one could see the flat sand shelf abruptly curving downward and plunging into the depths at an angle of about forty degrees. Clumps of *Halimeda* mottled the slope in increasing numbers farther down, but beyond the details were lost in a great blue pool of gloom. To the sides, as far as one could see, the sharp rim curved away in an arc like the rim of some weird undersea crater.

We hovered above the bottom, over the rim of the bowl. I didn't feel entirely comfortable swimming out much beyond it, nor, quite clearly, did Yani. He said as much. And now, as we looked down the darkened slope, I recalled actions and casual remarks of other island men that indicated a similar feeling. Out here, over the main lagoon basin, even the amphibious Ifalukians became creatures of the surface. For them the bowl of the lagoon was a broad highway for canoe travel between the islets, and a peaceful lake for fishing, but it was not quite a part of home. In large groups men did not hesitate to enter the deeper waters to lay their seines, but a man alone stayed in his canoe, or remained close to it in the water. I could understand this, at the level of feeling, now.

It is along the rim of the lagoon that man feels at ease and master of himself, if not of all he surveys. We are accustomed to solid ground, and in the water it is a comfort to have the bottom beneath one's feet or close at hand. The sandy lagoon shelf seems almost a wet extension of the land. Children shout and splash in the shallows, mothers wash their babies here, and about the patch reefs men spear those tasty jewels, the reef fishes.

Just out from the lagoon beach lie the dense, forest-green beds of turtle grass. On our aerial photographs they showed up as a dark strip along the lagoon shore, separated from the coconut trees by a white line of beach. Marston and I had done some speculating about this dark strip, even before we left Guam, for in the photographs it was traversed by a series of fine white lines, radiating out from shore too regularly to be "natural."

"Those lines . . . what are they?," we asked Josh Tracey. He shook his head dubiously; the dark stuff might possibly be consolidated reef material, but . . .

Neither Bates nor I had ever really seen an atoll from close up. Johnston and Kwajalein didn't count; to us they had been little more than airstrips in midocean. We theorized freely and without inhibitions. The dark stuff was probably beachrock, and the white lines might be grooves, worn by generations of islanders drawing their canoes across it at the same spots, going to and from the lagoon beach.

Theory and reality proved to be some little distance apart. On the atoll, we saw the dark band was the bed of turtle grass. And the white lines? They were little sandy pathways, worn in the beds by human feet; paths used by the people going to and from the waist-deep waters of the lagoon, usually for sanitary purposes.

Turtle grass is a name given to several flowering plants that have moved into the edges of tropic seas. The larger kinds on Ifaluk (*Enhalus, Thalassia*) really looked like reedy grasses, while a smaller species (*Halophila*) was short with leaves like butter paddles. Sea turtles eat at least two kinds, and we often surprised the big creatures browsing in the deeper parts of the beds. The startle-reflex, in fact, was often mutual.

Flowering plants as a group evolved on land and in fresh water, and most of them have stayed there. Eons of rain have flushed nearly all the salt from most terrestrial soils, even on parts of the earth that once were ancient seas, and to most land plants of today, salt in any quantity is a poison. True enough, some hardy species live in saline deserts and on the upper beaches of seashores. But only a few, like the mangrove, the eel grasses of our own coasts, and the various turtle grasses of warmer oceans, have really moved down into the sea.

Most of the turtle grass grows in the regions uncovered by the lowest tides. Here the beds form a rich marine association, with many sponges, sea-urchins, tunicates, and snails hidden among the green blades. We chose an area some distance from the nearest Ifalukian pathway and established a line marked with shiny can lids, extending out from shore. Along this line, every six feet, we sampled and recorded the plants and animals; I took the plants and the attached or slow-moving animals, while Bob and Ted Bayer handled the rest. As in the intertidal zones of most parts of the world the organisms were arranged in bands running parallel to the shore, those farthest out being the species that could least stand exposure at low tide.

The turtle grasses are firmly rooted. They anchor the sand in these beds, providing a stable bottom, a hiding place, and a rich source of food for some animals. In areas of shifting sand the beds are sparse or absent, and here, by comparison, the bottom seems almost a desert.

No question about it, the sandy floor in the lagoon shallows was full of fascinating holes. A hole in the ground is always a mute challenge to the field biologist, a sort of open invitation to investigate. It works the same way on small children.

There are two classic methods of determining what is in a hole. The basic techniques were worked out a long time ago by the cat and the dog, and modern biologists have only added refinements. The cat approach involves assuming a comfortable position and watching the hole for something to come out. A modern alternative is the trap. This method is well suited to the leisurely temperament, and is usually tried first, but when the watching is done in chilly water the span of attention may be pretty short. When patience is exhausted the biologist switches to the dog method; he tries to force the issue with shovel, forceps, or baited line. Each approach has its advantages, and the two are usually tried consecutively.

The smallest holes yielded to the feline approach. They were made by attractive little grey shrimps (*Synalpheus*) which could often be seen carrying sand out of their burrows. The animal's front pincers are flattened, and when held together they form an effective sort of carrying tray. The shrimp would appear at the mouth of its burrow bearing a great scoop of sand, and would carefully dump this a few inches away before returning. In the tunnels with the shrimps, two species of goby fishes lived as boarders. One was small and black and usually kept well inside; the other, protectively colored like the sandy bottom, would often sit on the sand just outside the hole, darting quickly inside at any disturbance.

Bob and Ted watched the larger sizes of holes till it was clear the canine technique was needed, then set to work with shovel and dip-net. The net went over the mouth of the hole, the shovel was sunk to one side and joggled. The local earthquake thus created sometimes sent the denizens shooting into the net. If not, the shovel bit in, cutting off the tunnel and scooping sand and burrow into the net, sometimes along with the inhabitants. It pays to be successful on the initial try, for the first load of the shovel clouds the water and subsequent work goes on in the marine equivalent of a smoke screen. Coaxing and profanity are often a help.

Excavations proceeded with some success. From the middle-sized holes, Bob and Ted got an interesting red shrimp (*Callianassa*). The largest holes might have been empty for all their efforts, but later in the summer Yani caught one of the diggers of these while we weren't watching. It was a big mantis shrimp, slender in front, broad-beamed, and brilliantly colored. These crustaceans are the weasels of the tropical reefs. Long, lean, and equipped with scythe-like forelimbs, they scoot swiftly along the bottom after prey and deal sudden death with slashing crushing blows.

We had never had a stretch of weather like this; day after day of glorious hot sun and the lightest of breezes. Only the smallest of scaly ripples stirred the lagoon surface, and the water was perfectly clear.

We had been working the lagoon patch reefs near shore, and waiting for the waters to clear enough for a good try at the bottom. We were not equipped for serious dredging, but we had some light gear and the chance now was too good to be missed. Ted Bayer, Yani, and I heaped our equipment in the BWUP and headed out for the bluer water beyond the sandy shelf. We had the sounding lead and line, a small dredge, a scoop-like metal bottom sampler, glass bottomed boxes and goggles, a graded series of wire mesh screens, and the usual assortment of bottles and canvas sample sacks. The Brunton compass went along as well, for taking azimuths and locating ourselves approximately in the lagoon. And of course some drinking coconuts for lunch. During the day we anchored at successive spots on a line across the lagoon basin, sampling the bottom here and there for depth, sediments, and organisms.

The bottom turned out to be mostly sand (great discovery). This, like the sand on the lagoon bottom at Bikini, consists mostly of the limy segments of the alga *Halimeda* and the shells of foraminiferan protozoa. Mixed with this are a host of miscellaneous calcareous fragments, and filtering through the whole is a powdery white silt. The debris here is not too different from the stuff one finds in crevices on the reef flats, but some of it is more finely divided.

Where does all the sand come from? Yani had asked the question one day when we were sitting on the windward shore, resting after an afternoon of tabulating the organisms found along a reef profile. I had walked down to the sand, scooped up a double handful, and spread it out on the rocks of the boulder ridge. Together we poked through it, separating out the things we could recognize from the nondescript crumbs of lime. And in the end the answer was pretty clear to both of us. The sand was "growing" out on the reef right in front of us; fragments of corals and limy seaweeds, bits of the shells of snails and clams, the skeletal parts of starfishes and sea-urchins, shells of the protozoan *Calcarina*—shaped like little two-faced sunflowers—and its relatives, and here and there the bones of birds and fishes.

One could almost see the wheels turn in Yani's head. He said, "Old men say they do not know where the sand comes from. Maybe the sea, deep down," he waved at the sea beyond the reef. But this was not what had impressed him. Later, on the trail home, he had put it into words.

"Sand cannot talk. But we ask the sand question, 'Where do you come from?,' and the sand answer us!" He was delighted.

The sand does not stay and form piles on the reefs. Some is carried outward toward the sea. The finer particles get swept over the reef flats, between the islets, and into the lagoon, where they soon settle to the bottom in the quieter waters. Here the sand may become still finer by abrasion, by passage through the guts of such detritus eaters as the sea-cucumbers, and perhaps by slow solution. Not all of the finest silt is formed this way, however. Certain of the reef fishes feed on living coral, and have curious crushing teeth adapted for nibbling off chunks of the stony stuff. Some of this is reduced to fine material passing through the digestive tract. When these fishes defecate they spew out a cloud of fine white particles which settles slowly to the bottom to form calcareous ooze.

Today we dredged up quantities of the loose material from the surface of the lagoon floor, and washed this through a series of graded screens that separated things roughly according to particle size, whether alive or dead. There were large numbers of tiny clams, and small snail shells inhabited by hermit crabs. The clams feed on plankton and detritus suspended in the water, and the hermit crabs are mostly scavengers. Judging from the size of the population, both appeared to have good pickings on the bottom.

The dredge didn't behave as well as we had hoped. It was a light portable affair, ideal from the point of view of shipping and of handling in a skiff, but not heavy enough to get a good bite into the bottom. We got good samples of the surface material, but things under the surface were pretty safe from it. The bottom sampler behaved much better, and dragged up not only sand but quite a bit of seaweed and numerous fragments of coral from isolated patch reefs on the bottom.

The lagoon bottom proved to be more irregular than we had supposed, though the Hydrographic Office chart of Ifaluk, based on a Japanese sketch survey in 1921, showed depth variations of four to eleven fathoms in its few soundings. The deepest areas formed a broken ring, extending in toward the center from the base of the lagoon slope, while centrally the floor rose in a shallower mound. The mound could be spotted from shore, for the water here was a paler blue than that around it. Now we could see that this mound, too, undulated in a series of low hummocks and ridges, interspersed with shallow valleys and flatter sea plains. The basins between the hills seemed relatively naked sandy stretches, while the hummocks themselves bore dark patches of material, visible but not readily identifiable from the surface. We got intrigued with the little scraps of things that kept coming up in the dredge and sampler, and decided to get a closer look.

We anchored the BWUP over a likely looking sandy knoll where the sounding lead told us the depth was only six fathoms, put on our goggles, and slipped over the side into the water.

It takes a while to adjust to the world of water, after the brilliance of the surface sun and the clarity of the atoll air above. Here the world is a pale green, and even in clean waters the range of vision is less than a hundred feet. Beyond this the sunlight is scattered and objects merge and fade, curtained by the still, bright mist.

We hung in the water at the surface and looked—at the bottom and on all sides—trying to spot any larger moving shadows that might be drifting in the opalescence at the borders of vision. There were none.

We went for the bottom. Things seemed to get clearer with every stroke, and it was soon apparent that the dark area on the mound below us was a bed of the seaweed *Halimeda*. Individual plants were spaced about six inches apart, and the whole formed a great green rug on the whitened floor of sand. Clearly, then, some of the lagoon sand was being formed right in place. Ted and I couldn't quite make the bottom, but we could see Yani down below us, hanging on to the seaweed with one hand and busily tearing loose samples with the other. He looked up and blew a bubble of air at us before we turned away and surfaced, lungs ready to burst. Half a minute later he was up by the BWUP with a canvas sack of algae and other materials from the bottom.

We swam around the borders of the bed, trying to estimate its size. Distances are hard to judge underwater, or right at the surface, and finally it seemed best for one of us to stay at the boat. Ted was elected. Yani and I swam out to points where we were directly over the edges of the algal bed, and Ted tried to estimate our distances from the boat. We circled the bed this way, and it seemed an irregular ovoid, roughly 230 by 250 feet. On the sand near one edge lay one of the monstrous sea cucumbers, *Thelenota*, its warty body curved in a large half-circle, going about its leisurely task of ingesting sand for the organic matter in it. Not far off a pair of large brown boxfishes drifted lazily just above the bottom, their curious trunklike forms casting blunt shadows on the dark rug of algae. Then the underwater world darkened suddenly as a cloud sailed like a great white canoe across the noonday sun. We climbed into the BWUP again and pulled the dredge across the algal mat, snipping off bits of seaweed at the surface. But Yani had already done a much more effective job of sampling the bottom.

The evening discussion was well along. We had started with the work of the past day, had probably digressed at least once on the general subject of women, and had come back at last to a question on the gross anatomy of the atoll. This time it was the reason for the curious profile of the lagoon floor, with its shelf around the edge, its steep lagoon slope, and its deeper undulating sandy bottom. As usual, we were looking to Josh Tracey for an answer, or at least a part of one.

Josh didn't like being forced into the role of an oracle on atolls. He pointed out that he was widely travelled in the immediate environs of Bikini atoll, which differed from Ifaluk in a number of ways, and that we were all authorities on atolls—*an* atoll, anyway. But, as usual, Josh had something to say. The whole problem was tied up, not only with the question of where the sand was formed, but also with how water circulated in the lagoon.

How did it circulate, anyway? Getting a good answer might be a tough problem, for such research at Bikini had required a sizeable team of observers, dye markers to trace water movements, ships, aircraft, and working scale models of the lagoon. Still, our lagoon was a lot smaller, and Josh thought we might learn something by combining observations of our own with information from the observant Ifalukians. He suggested we have a crack at determining what happened at the ship pass during a cycle of tides. We agreed, and next morning Josh, Arnow, Yani, and I took the BWUP over for a look.

The ship pass on the south of Ifaluk is the only real channel through the circular atoll reef. The "Sailing Directions for the Pacific Islands," Vol. 1, put out by the Navy Hydrographic Office, has the following to say about it. "Between the two southernmost (islets) . . . is a shoal passage available to small boats; it is also very narrow due to a reef immediately inside. A small vessel entered the lagoon in 1950 via this passage, and anchored off the southwestern end of (Falarik) Island, the northernmost island of the group, in a depth of eight fathoms. It was reported that the passage had a depth of about three fathoms and was about fifty yards wide. A coral head with a depth of 1¼ fathoms was located on the eastern side of the passage and other coral heads were located throughout the passage." Not much of a pass for ships, all things considered, and more the credit to Captain Cowart for shoe-horning the NETTLE in and out again without a scratch.

We stopped first over one of the great "coral heads" that make the passage a dangerous one for ships. It was a tall coral knoll, shaped like a huge blunt tooth, and topped with the upright blades of the green stinging hydrocoral *Millepora*. The surface was nearly awash, for the tide was fairly low and still ebbing.

There were several of these coral knolls, much alike, their steep sides festooned with colonies of living coral and graceful fronds of algae streaming with the tidal current. Between these well-spaced hazards to navigation lay the channel bottom, in some places nearly forty feet down, its irregular gloomy surface covered with massive heads and antlers of coral.

We took a series of soundings to get an idea of the cross-sectional area of the pass at this point, and anchored in the center. Then we put down the sounding line and tied one end to the boat. The sounding line was a half-inch manila line, weighted heavily at one end. We had tied short strips of cheesecloth at one fathom intervals along the line, hoping these would stream out with the current to show us the direction of water flow at all levels in the channel. The method left something to be desired. The streamers went with the current alright, but the coral knolls nearby caused some local eddies, and from time to time the streamers flickered and reversed direction.

Then someone had the bright idea of using "shark chasers" for dye markers in the water. We promptly tried it. The idea worked beautifully. We were delighted at last to find a use for the chasers, for we had dozens of them in our supplies.

A shark chaser, or shark repellent unit, comes in a waterproof yellow packet about the size of a bar of laundry soap. A man who has one, and feels the need for it, has only to rip down a tab on the front, and the chaser goes into action. The contents, a cloth package, drops down into the water and hangs below his feet at the end of a tape, and the water around the bag quickly clouds up with a dark purple dye.

It works this way, at least in theory. Sharks which are not particularly excited cruise around slowly and hunt mainly by scent, or its underwater equivalent. A chemical in the chaser interferes with the shark's sense of smell. However when close to food or when excited, sharks begin to depend to a greater extent on sight, and are likely to strike at any moving object regardless of odor. Shark eyesight isn't too good, and the purple dye contained in the chaser clouds the water enough to block shark vision fairly effectively.

Trouble is, the dye pretty effectively interferes with the underwater vision of biologists too. Working conditions for biologists and sharks aren't too different—we're a predatory lot—and it usually seemed easier (not to mention safer) to pick relatively sharkless areas for work than to try chasing the beasts off their home grounds. Here in Ifaluk pass, however, the shark gadgets were most useful. The dye streamed away in clouds with the current, clearly distinguishing eddies from the main flow.

The tidal level dropped steadily and water continued to pour out of the lagoon through the pass, keeping the anchor rope taut and the skiff in the center of the channel. The rate of flow seemed considerable, and we made regular measurements of this by the "Dutchman's Log" method. At its simplest, all you need to do is drop a chip off one end of the boat and time it along a measured distance, in this case the length of the boat.

Low tide was supposed to come at about 1:40 P.M. that day, according to the tide table predictions for Woleai island, only forty miles away. We noted water level on outcroppings of the reef on the east side of the pass and along the shores of Ella islet on the west. The low tide hour came and went with the water level still dropping.

Then Ted Arnow suggested that perhaps the chips and scraps of notebook paper we had been using for timing the flow rate in the channel were just getting surface currents, which were somewhat subject to the wind. He thought it would be a fine idea if Yani and I would get into the water, hang more or less vertically, and allow ourselves

to be timed as we drifted past the boat. We did, and the measurements turned out much as they had when we used scraps of paper.

Another hour, and now periodic checks of water level on the rocks
and shores nearby showed that the tide had turned, and was slowly
rising. Yet flow in the channel was still toward the sea, and the dye
from the shark chasers continued to stream southward to the open
ocean.

This was all very confusing, and not at all what we had expected.
On the face of it, when the tide was rising water ought to stream into
the lagoon along all possible access routes—over the reefs and in
through the channel. Many times we had felt these incoming tidal
currents pouring in over the northern and western reefs. Josh and
Arnow talked learnedly about cross-sectional areas, drainage rates,
heads of water, and such. The general hypothesis at this stage seemed
to be that as the general level of the sea dropped with the tide, the
lagoon level went down more slowly; that there was a tidal lag in the
lagoon due to lack of adequate drainage channels. The lagoon, then,
with its head of water, would continue to drain even past the ebb
and while the waters rose in the sea outside, until levels in the sea
and lagoon were again equalized. Flow in the ship pass should then
cease for a period, and finally reverse. A simple problem, shrewdly
resolved.

Another hour. The current seemed to be slacking off a bit, and Yani
and I were called on to act as human drift bottles once more. And
then, halfway through the first drift, I saw down below me the biggest
bony fish I'd seen in all the time on Ifaluk. I called excitedly to Yani,
and we peered down at the thing—a big wrasse (*Cheilinus*). It was
a Mam, he said, good to eat but rarely taken by the islanders because
of its large size and preference for deeper waters. It looked a bit like
an enormous bass, perhaps five feet long. We watched, and soon it
was joined by another fair sized fish, a yard long and with a bulldog
head—some sort of a grouper. Yani pointed it out, a Taiyau, and
said that when this type got bigger it was dangerous, and sometimes
bit people. We watched, the drift observation forgotten.

Then a third fish, larger than the others, appeared out of nowhere
below us. Yani hollered "Paro!," and a moment later we were both

LEFT The vegetation screen on the ocean side of Falarik was dominated by Scaevola and Messerschmidia.

HT The boulder ridge it-
： was covered with stilt-
ted Pandanus and a tough
n.

LEFT Inland from the boulder ridge was the mixed growth of the boondocks.

Women's work included the weaving of skirts and loin cloths; and the cultivation of taro in the rich soil of the bwol.

ABOVE Preparing breadfruit: pots, pans and buckets were much appreciated on Ifaluk.

RIGHT One of the varieties of breadfruit ("mai"), called "welige sol."

No metal was available on the Pacific Islands before Western contact: all tools were made of shell or wood.

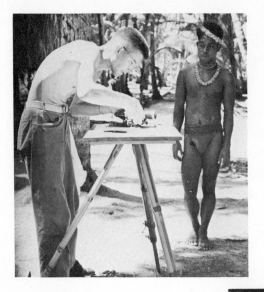

LEFT Josh Tracey made a geological survey of the atoll. PHOTO BY BAYER

BELOW Ted Bayer (here with Yani) came to Ifaluk to study the marine invertebrates.

LOWER RIGHT Bob Harry was after fish and he had all of the equipment, including an aqualung. PHOTO BY BAYER

BELOW Ted Arnow promptly set up a tide gauge for his water level studies. PHOTO BY HARRY

in the boat. I haven't the slightest recollection of any intervening time, nor had Josh and Arnow. They said they heard a yell, felt the BWUP rock sharply, and there we were on the floorboards.

We looked down over the side. The shark swam about slowly near the bottom, showing interest neither in the boat nor in the other large fishes down below. It nosed gracefully near the edges of the cloud of dye streaming from the shark chasers, but didn't enter it, and drifted off behind a coral knoll. Arnow immediately pointed out that the drift measurement had not been completed to his satisfaction, but we looked around in vain for a volunteer.

The outward current, which had slackened noticeably for a period, picked up again, till water was pouring out of the lagoon toward the open sea. And still the tidal level rose rapidly. The wind picked up, too, and it began to rain. Then it began to get dark. When we were thoroughly soaked and chilled we headed back for home, low tide more than two hours past and the current still streaming outward toward the south, in defiance of our expectations though no doubt in accordance with the laws of physics.

Hypotheses are useful things to the scientist. They represent preliminary educated guesses at answers to problems or explanations of relationships. An initial hypothesis is often a crude thing, but it is a concept that can be checked and replaced or modified as information accumulates. It serves as a sort of central thought around which the facts may be grouped, and through which the relations between the facts become clearer. Refined hypotheses that stand the tests and moreover allow us to predict new facts correctly, can be nudged over a rather arbitrary line into the class of scientific theory.

With our scanty information, and the further information the men of Ifaluk were able to give us on the direction and strength of water flow over the reefs and through the pass, we can set up a preliminary working hypothesis as to what is happening.

There does seem to be a real tidal lag in the lagoon. When the ebbing tide drops below the level of the ring of reefs and islets, water trapped in the lagoon can only spill out by way of the relatively narrow southern ship pass and over the lowest sections of the reef. As a result, at low tide there is still a head of water in the lagoon, and outflow at the pass continues for a time even after the sea outside has begun to rise again. On a very calm day, when the level of the water outside reaches the level in the lagoon again, outflow in the channel ceases, and soon shifts to an inflow.

But when the wind is from the north or west, as it often is during the summer season, this doesn't happen. Instead, when the water levels in ocean and lagoon are equalized, the whole system begins to act like a broad river. Waters are heaped by the breaking waves onto the plains of the northern and western reefs, and here they attain a mean level slightly above that of either the lagoon or the surrounding sea. This elevated sheet or head of water tends to flow downhill following the path of least resistance. Some returns immediately to the outer sea, passing down along radiating grooves in the reef front. But more of it sweeps inward across the bare reef flat toward the lagoon, seeking its own level, and driven as well by the winds and successive waves behind. The flow appears sufficient to maintain an outward current at the southern ship channel even in the face of a rising tide. Josh estimated the volume of the lagoon at roughly 1.1 billion cubic feet, and the inflow over the northwestern reef on a sample day at over 900 million cubic feet per day. Under these conditions much of the water in the lagoon would be replaced daily, and even in windless periods the lagoon probably never suffers from stagnation.

This picture of lagoon circulation leads us to a possible explanation of the general contour of the sandy-floored lagoon. The bulk of the atoll's sand forms on the reefs or in the lagoon itself. Waves beat in over the reefs from all sides of the atoll when the tide is in, driving particles across the reefs toward the lagoon. Where islets intervene, the sand contributes to them; where none are present, the particles move on. The finer materials are carried farthest inward, transported beyond the zones of severe wave action by the powerful incoming currents on a rising tide. True, some particles are also carried outward by drainage down the reef front and by the lesser currents of the early ebb tide, but the quantity is relatively small. The net movement of reef sand is inward, toward the lagoon. Here, reaching the quieter waters, it comes to rest on the bottom. At the lagoonward ends of channels between close-set islets it builds sandy deltas; elsewhere it deposits to form the broad lagoon shelf—really an extended circular delta. If this is correct, then over the centuries, the sandy lagoon shelf is growing broader, marching slowly toward the center of the lagoon.

And meanwhile, in the central basin of the lagoon, more sand is being formed by the limy seaweeds and shelled organisms that live there on the sea floor. Of these, the seaweed *Halimeda stuposa* is the most important, for great beds of this plant dominate the shallow knolls and ridges of the bottom. Are these mounds simply more favorable spots for algal growth, since they receive more light and perhaps a freer circulation of the bottom waters? Scattered exposed coral ledges near the edges of the mounds, noted by Bob Rofen, suggest that the elevations represent old, buried coral formations. Whatever lies below the sand, the present mounds are probably being elevated still further by growth and disintegration of the algae in the seaweed beds, and the lagoon floor contours may be both a cause and effect of algal growth.

Not all of the sand remains in the lagoon. Some must be stirred occasionally by currents and the effects of surface waves on the lagoon in storms; some is again swept outward through the ship pass and, to a lesser degree, over the low section of reef between Elangalap and Ella, for there are sandy deposits on the bottom outside the atoll in these places. But the indications are that sand enters, and forms in, the lagoon, faster than it leaves.

Thus, on this tiny atoll, it looks as though the lagoon with its central basin is gradually filling up. Perhaps the men of a future millennium may find the lagoon a shallows, all the way across.

If this should happen, two spirits should be pleased. The shade of Darwin will nod sagely at another of his predictions come to pass. And my ghost will say to Yani's, "Sure, I'll swim across the lagoon to Elangalap!" I wouldn't want to bet on his reply.

CHAPTER XIII

SOMETHING OF
THE PAST

THE MORNING after our session at the ship pass we wakened at 6:45 to find the METOMKIN anchored off Ella, and the launch already puttering across the lagoon. We rolled out of bed in a hurry, especially Josh and Arnow. The ship was two days early, and they had neither packed nor finished their work. Quickly we pulled on shorts and went down to meet the boat.

It beached and the passengers splashed ashore. In charge this trip was Mr. Kim, agricultural expert for the Yap District of the Trust Territory, a figure of solid competence carved in mahogany. Like myself, he was a graduate of the University of Hawaii. He joined us for coffee in the Fan Nap before making his rounds, and suggested Josh see the Captain of the METOMKIN about the possibility of a few more days on Ifaluk. Josh boarded the launch, and the rest of us plunged into the work that must be done if the ship were to leave for good that day.

Josh was back in a couple of hours. It had taken some persuasive argument, but the Captain had at last agreed to go on to Sorol island and to return in two days to Ifaluk. Things settled down somewhat, and in a few hours the METOMKIN was gone again.

The next two days were busy ones, in spite of intermittent rains. There were short trips to check specific geological points, and interrogations of patient Ifalukians. Arnow set up a water-level recorder to run for several weeks in a nearby well. We all wrote letters, for this was the last chance to get word out from Ifaluk before our final departure in November.

164

On the first evening we gathered for supper at Toroman's house near the Falarik-Falalap channel at the south end of Rauau village. It was a small party, for just the chiefs and ourselves, and the food was already laid on mats spread on Toroman's immaculate lawn. There were two chickens, bundled in steaming leaves, and bowls of taro cooked in coconut cream. Wolpaitik contributed a small bottle of tubwa.

Maroligar, who appeared to be giving the party jointly with Toroman, unwrapped the birds and carved. His dissecting technique had little in common with our own elaborate carving ritual; he simply grabbed the birds in two hands and tore them apart. They were a bit underdone, and the great flight muscles of the breast peeled off along with the wings. Maroligar passed the pieces around with a "Family, please hold back" look at his colleagues. The meat was tough and stringy, but it was our first fresh chicken in months and it went down easily. After a polite interval we excused ourselves to get in some evening work.

Arnow came away from the party convinced that Toroman was low man on the chiefly pole. He reviewed the evidence, which here concerned the distribution of the drinks. Being concerned with potable fluids in a professional way, Arnow had eyed the bottle from the start; clearly there would not be enough for a full round unless the snorts were very short. As guests, we had been served first. Fagolier had been offered a glass and had politely declined. Maroligar took a bit, and that left very little. Wolpaitik had up-ended and killed the bottle without further ado. Ted felt that Toroman, if he were really number three in the chiefly hierarchy, should have rated at least a share of the dregs.

Perhaps so, but Arnow's argument seemed a bit thin. I took the opposite side. We didn't know for a fact that Ifaluk drank by rank. It was, after all, Wolpaitik's own bottle, and it was he who poured. Moreover Toroman was sitting some little distance away, in a poor position to defend his interests. Finally, it seemed quite in character for Wolpaitik to make sure he got his share. We had always imagined the portly chief as a sort of small-town, insecure Henry VIII, atypically gross and selfish for a man of Ifaluk.

These arguments got nowhere with Arnow, and I resolved to ask Tom again sometime about the relative status of the chiefs. Sure enough, Toroman outranked Wolpaitik.

The day the METOMKIN was due passed without a sign of her. At last, about dusk, the people sighted a light off Elangalap, and by nightfall the ship had dropped her hook off Ella. We marked the landing beach with Coleman lanterns and flashlights as the launch, searchlight sweeping the water from her prow, made a quick trip across the lagoon. We loaded the gear. The chiefs brought a large pile of green coconuts and some mar as gifts from the atoll to whatever Micronesian passengers might be riding aboard the METOMKIN. A crowded and confused good-bye, and the boat was only a light and a sound receding over the black water.

Feeling rather let down, we wandered back to the Fan Nap and sat around the old crate that served as a table in our dining nook, making talk and finishing a small bottle of tubwa that Tom had given us earlier. The place seemed empty without Josh and Arnow, as it had for a time without Bates and Burrows. I was in a "permanent party" mood again, and the work that remained to be done on the atoll seemed to stretch before us without end. We took turns at playing Pollyanna, but there was a heaviness in the air that was not easily dispelled.

There may be an old wives' saying, "When down in the dumps, clean house." If there isn't, there should be. We needed some sort of a change to symbolize a new beginning. The next day was a gorgeous Sunday. Warm brilliance streamed from a molten sun, and the breeze tossed the green skirts of the palms in a carefree dance. We celebrated by turning the Fan Nap upside down.

It started with Bob and Ted moving their sleeping gear from the tent into the house. Bob took over the bed across from mine, occupied earlier by Burrows and then Arnow. Ted Bayer fell heir to Marston's cot, which Josh had moved to the very front of the building to make more space. The work tables were cleared of geological leftovers and reloaded for marine work. We swept the sleeping area and ripped the old coconut mats from the front of the house, dispelling the gloom of weeks with a flood of light from the west. Maroligar walked by outside and smiled his approval; the rains, he said, should be nearly over, and from now on the winds would blow from the east.

The sunlight streaming in the tidy front of the house only served to emphasize the mess that prevailed at the back. I was used to it. There had been order in the beginning, and makeshift cleanups now and then on rainy days, but to face it, we hadn't had the instincts and interests of housekeepers. The food supplies, for example; cardboard cartons of cans, once stacked neatly by Ted Burrows in open crates placed on their sides, were in confusion. We had used so many cans that the cartons were collapsed one into another, and what we wanted was always near the bottom just above the sauerkraut. It looked as though the eatables might conveniently be restowed in half the space. Bob and Ted pitched in, and soon things were in beautiful order. Cans were consolidated and rearranged according to genus and species of contents; one could see at a glance what remained, and reach things without moving a box. The old unwieldy vegetable crate was emptied and carried outside, making space for Ted's work table across from mine.

From here efforts extended to the rest of the house and slowly a logical order replaced the mnemonic filing system. Bob discovered three brand new Coleman lanterns in a dark corner, raising our total to seven in working order. A new supply of dried fruit materialized in a tin box I had been sure contained nothing but some butterscotch puddings which had been included especially for Bob Rofen. The puddings themselves remained in hiding.

During the cleanup we kept a special eye for Ted Burrows' false teeth, which had disappeared one day near the end of his stay. Ted had evolved a complex hypothesis to account for the loss; probably a rat had stolen the plate, and then, finding itself under sudden attack by a monitor lizard, had dropped the dentures down a land-crab hole. The teeth never did show up; I like to think they lie bedded with ancient tools of shell, waiting to puzzle some archeologist of the far future.

When the work was done, the wives of our helpers brought fresh green coconut mats to replace the worn ones on the dirt floor. We laid them carefully and stood back to admire the effect. Light and breezy now, neat and clean, the Fan Nap seemed again the tropical palace it really was, and one of the pleasantest things about it was that Bob and Ted had done practically all the work. The sunshine, the therapy of the new broom, and the new look of the house were a spring tonic to the spirit. There was a feeling of starting afresh on a new expedition. A shade of Marston's presence, lounging in the corner, stared into my cerebral cortex with elevated eyebrows. "Ah," it said with a pleased smile, "the manic phase again."

We had a swim, ate lunch, and I worked over notes for a couple of hours, then relaxed at my table, mulling over past work and future projects. The little clock beside me ticked softly, each sound a reminder of the flow of time, of precious minutes streaming endlessly into the past.

Precious minutes? I could look out under the fringe of thatch and see men reclining in the shade of Rolong canoe house, resting in the drowsy warmth, chatting easily, and swatting an occasional fly or copra bug. Where was their sense of urgency, of opportunity ungrasped, of life's numbered hours slipping by? And where, for that matter, was mine? Already we had lived here a pleasant lifetime, and our pickup date of November 10th seemed impossibly remote. There was no time here but the present, and the present was eternity.

This proved a distracting line of thought. My rationalizing apparatus immediately whispered that on Sundays the Pacific Science Board permitted distracting thoughts, in moderation of course. The other neurons played with the concept of subjective time as a cultural and situational variable, conditioned by a host of different factors. Perhaps where days and generations followed one another in changeless replication, past and future tended to merge with the present to create in the mind a timeless world. Ifaluk had a past, but beyond a generation it wasn't much discussed; there would be a future, but nobody worried much about that, either.

Yet there *had* been changes on Ifaluk, brought about by outside cultural contacts, and more changes would surely come. I reached for the monograph on Ifaluk by Burrows and Spiro, and read over the section on "Foreign Relations." When Yani came by a few minutes later, we walked over to talk to Tom and Toroman. It was not so much to gain new facts, for Burrows had unearthed many of these in song, legend, and human memory here, and in the records of the West. It was more to discover some feeling for the past, some sense of history in a land that seemed forever in the here and now. Perhaps it was a search for a sense of space as well, for geographical limits can be confining to human thought, and with the rest of the world out of sight it sometimes slipped from mind as well. Too often we tended to think of Ifaluk as a microcosmic whole, isolated and self-sufficient, proud and independent, its horizon the outer boundary of reality.

I admit this was a pleasant state of mind, but of course it simply wasn't true. Even for Ifaluk the links to the world were there, though our knowledge of them, based on accounts of recent anthropologists and the earlier explorers, is only fragmentary.

For no one knows how long, Ifaluk was a small unit in what anthropologists call the "Yap Empire." At its top, the village of Gatchepar on Yap played the role of father to the family of inhabited atolls strewn in the trackless immensities of blue from Yap to Truk. The outlying empire was a loose-knit thing; fourteen coral specks totalling less than a dozen square miles of land in some 200,000 of wind-swept ocean, and only frail canoes and sturdy men with sentiments and fears to link the scattered parts. The wonder is that it ever started and cohered at all. The ties of empire served mainly to govern a flow of gifts, tributes, and religious offerings from the subordinate islands to the ruling chiefs of Gatchepar. A smaller series of gifts flowed the other way, and at least so far as Ifaluk was concerned, there was no external control over purely internal affairs.

Within the empire was a chain of command, complicated in that it extended through certain family groupings, that passed from Yap to Ulithi atoll, and from here through sparsely branching lines of communication out to the islands lying farthest to the east. For Ifaluk the orders of the Gatchepar chiefs went from Yap to Ulithi to Woleai to Ifaluk, which passed them in turn to Lamotrek, next in line. For the workings of the system in outlying islands we are indebted to anthropologist William Lessa, who worked on Ulithi, and to Ted Burrows.

Every two or three years, in the olden days, the great sailing canoes of the far flung atolls would gather in the huge lagoon at Ulithi, a pigmy foreshadowing of the American naval fleets that massed here in World War II. Ifaluk and most of the other atolls sent one canoe each, though by the middle of the 19th century the four most distant atolls of the empire brought their gifts only as far as Satawal, which forwarded them on. Woleai and Ulithi each sent eight canoes, one for each of their larger islets; Fais, whose canoes lacked sails, sent none, nor was there a canoe from Sorol Island, where the arts of navigation were poorly known or had been lost. Once assembled, the fleet of twenty-two canoes would sail for Yap, led by a Captain from Ulithi, and bearing rope, pandanus mats, coconut oil, the fine loin-cloths of Ulithi, and a sort of coconut candy. Returning, the canoes carried the lesser gifts of Yap; food, combs, bamboo, red turmeric, and other goods.

How and when did these tribute voyages begin?, we asked, and in answer there were only shakes of heads; there are legends that Ifaluk was originally populated from Yap, but the real story lies hidden in that forgotten past that Ifaluk calls the "before-before-before," and modern investigations have so far thrown little light on the origin and duration of the Yap Empire.

For the rest of Ifaluk's history we have only its songs commemorating deeds of past heroes like Maur and Mailias, and the scattered records left by European explorers and missionaries in the western Carolines. Only the latter can be assigned a place in the stream of time.

The discovery of the New World by Columbus in 1492, and the voyage of Vasco da Gama around the Cape of Good Hope to the East Indies in 1497 opened up new vistas for Europe, and slowly the hands of the West reached out to grasp the world. Soon the first fingers probed the realm of Oceania. Ferdinand Magellan crossed the Pacific to discover the Marianas and die in the Philippines in 1521, but the voyage was completed by one of his ships, and the world of the seafaring man became a globe. Magellan's course had taken him to the north of most of the southern island groups except the Marquesas, and with remarkable ill-luck he had encountered only two small, desolate islets on his entire trip from South America to Guam.

Meanwhile, the Portuguese had already settled in the East Indies.

About 1526, some five years after Magellan's death, a Portuguese voyager, Diogo da Rocha, entered the Pacific from the east and discovered what may have been Yap and Ulithi, or the Palau Islands. And now two Spanish expeditions set out to follow Magellan's path, one from Spain under Don Garcia Jofre de Loyasa, the other dispatched by Cortez from Zacatula, Mexico, under Alvaro de Saavedra. Both apparently sighted the Marshall Islands, and Saavedra in 1528 seems to have seen some of the Carolines on the first of two unsuccessful attempts to return to the New World.

Spain established itself in Guam and the Philippines, as brutally as it had in the Americas, and for nearly two centuries Guam was important chiefly as a port for Spanish galleons sailing between Manila and the New World. There were only sporadic attempts at further exploration, but bits of the Carolines or Palaus were probably seen by Villalobos, Arellano, Legazpi, Sir Francis Drake, Mendana and Quiros, Shapenham, ships of the Nassau fleet, Lazeano, and Rodriguez in the period 1543 to 1696. Among these voyagers it is difficult to be sure who saw which islands, for localities and native place names were recorded poorly or not at all. It is Admiral Lazeano's name for Yap ("Carolina," in honor of Carlos II of Spain) which gradually came to be applied to the Caroline group as a whole, largely because no one could tell one island from another in this area. With American colonies and wars at home, Spain's hands were full. While islands to the south were now known, the galleons considered them a hazard to navigation, and most ships kept to a northerly route. For a long period they were neglected and almost forgotten.

It was the Jesuit priests who revived an interest in the scattered bits of land to the south. Two canoes of Fais islanders put in at Samar in the Philippines in December of 1696. The thirty-five people aboard were nearly starved, for they had been adrift for seventy days, living on rainwater and such fish as they could catch in their basket traps. A priest, Father Paul Clain, gathered from them a list of thirty-two Caroline island names, in which "Yfaluc" appears for the first time in western records. The travellers reported that all but three of the islands named were densely populated, and all were ruled by a high chief on Lamurrec (Lamotrek), the most important island. Father André Ser-

rano made a very crude chart of the islands, based on native arrangements of pebbles on the sand. This was presented to Pope Clement XI,
and he approved a program of missionary work in the islands. Between 1697 and 1721 several Spanish ships sailed for the Palaus and
Carolines. Two priests were landed with a small party at Sonsorol, but
the ship, unable to anchor there, was forced to leave them. They were
never heard from again, though unsuccessful rescue attempts were
made from time to time. In reading these old accounts, one realizes
that the European sailing ships of the time were almost as much at
the mercy of the elements as the canoes of the islanders themselves.

The next bits of information on the western Carolines appear in a
letter of March 22, 1722, from Jesuit Father Juan Antonio Cantova to
the confessor of the King of Spain. The priest was stationed on Guam,
and in mid-June, 1721, two canoes of Faraulap islanders put in there.
The fifteen men, eight women, and seven children aboard had been
making for Woleai, but had been driven far to the north. They were
tattooed, had their ears pierced for wearing flowers, and appeared of
mixed ancestry. They wished to provision their canoes and return but
the Governor of Guam had them detained, hoping to persuade them to
lead missionaries back to the islands from which they came. Father
Cantova befriended the voyagers, learned their language, and recorded
many details about them. He was told that their islands were divided
into five provinces, corresponding roughly to (1) the Truk group, (2)
the islands between Truk and Ulithi, (3) the Ulithi-Fais-Sorol region,
(4) the Yap Islands, and (5) the Palau Islands. The second province,
with fourteen of its twenty-six islands and reefs heavily populated, included the "important" atolls of Woleai, Lamotrek, Satawal, Ifaluk,
Euarupik, and Faraulap, the principal islands being Woleai and Lamotrek. Cantova compiled from the islanders the first usable chart of the
Carolines, and for nearly a century it was scarcely improved upon.
"Ifeluc" appears on it in approximately the right location in relation to
neighboring islands. Father Cantova made trips to Ulithi in 1722 and
again in 1731, the second time landing with soldiers and cannon.
Hardly was the Spanish ship that had brought them out of sight before the Ulithians set upon the priest and his party and destroyed
them. News of the brutal Spanish treatment of the people of Guam

had doubtless long since spread to the Carolines, and Ulithi wanted none of it.

This marked the end of Spanish attempts to do anything with the smaller islands of the Carolines. According to a later (Protestant) missionary account, the priests, ". . . having informed themselves of the general poverty of the islands, and certain that they could never be of value to the Spanish monarchy, . . . quitted them, and since that time they have been totally neglected." Ifaluk, as far as we can tell, was never seen or visited.

Europe really discovered the Pacific as the 18th century advanced. Explorers fanned out to cover the whole vast ocean, and the tracks of their voyages form a tangled spiderweb on the map. Greatest of the navigators was Captain Cook, and while many followed later, by the time of his death in 1779 nearly all the major island groups in the Pacific had been located by the West.

"Discovery" has a special meaning to the European explorer and geographer; credit for finding an island goes to the man who first visits and records a recognizable location or description of the place. Thus for the Carolines it mattered no whit that the islanders had been there for millennia; most of the atolls here were not "discovered" till the period 1773–1828. Already the early whalers, the island traders, and beachcombers had entered the Pacific, and on their heels came the first Protestant missionaries. It was one of these, Captain James Wilson, who "found" Ifaluk; the discovery itself was a fleeting incident in an historic voyage.

Wilson was born in Newcastle, England, youngest son in a family of nineteen. As a youth he shipped with his Captain father, stepping ashore in his middle teens to fight with the British at Bunker Hill. Soon he had his own ship, and as a trader he did not seek the peaceful byways. He turned to the Indies, and was soon running guns and stores past the French blockade of the Madras coast. Captured ashore with a Highland regiment, he spent twenty-two months in irons in the fortress of Hyder Ali, Moslem ally of the French, where four out of five of his fellow prisoners died. Released at last, he rejoined the Indies trade, earning wealth for retirement in Hampshire at the ripe old age of thirty-six.

It seems scarcely the background for a missionary. Never a pious man, Wilson was described by friends of the period as "a skeptic," "a Deist of the Old School," and "an Infidel in principle." A Baptist missionary with whom he sailed back to England once remarked to the mate that he would "have much more hope of converting the Laskars to Christianity than Captain Wilson." Wilson is even said to have bragged, "I have never met a clergyman yet whom I could not foil in a quarter of an hour." His penchant for religious argument was to be his undoing.

In Hampshire he met another retired ship's master, one Captain Simms. A godly but inarticulate man, Simms tired of losing arguments to Wilson, and one evening introduced him to a young minister, Mr. Griffen of Portsea. A discussion was soon underway, and Captain Simms withdrew discretely from the garden. It is said that the conversation lasted much longer than a quarter of an hour, and was continued at a later date, but Wilson had met his match. He was gathered to the fold in 1796.

It was a critical date. The London Missionary Society, founded the year before, was on fire to spread the gospel to the heathen. One of its founders, Dr. Haweis, Rector of All Saints at Aldwinkle, proclaimed the feeling with eloquence: "The field before us is immense! O that we could enter at a thousand gates!—that every limb were a tongue, and every tongue a trumpet, to spread the joyful sound!" There remained only to settle on a place to start, and the Society decided to begin its work in the South Sea Islands.

When the Society issued its call for volunteers to follow in the wake of Captain Cook, James Wilson was the first to step forward. The ship DUFF was purchased in June for 5000 pounds, and on August 10, 1796, Wilson sailed from the Thames with thirty male missionaries, six wives, three children (the youngest only sixteen months), a mate, and a crew of twenty. His orders read: "That a mission be undertaken to Otaheite, the Friendly Islands, the Marquesas, the Sandwich, and the Pelew Islands . . . as far as may be practicable and expedient."

The voyage took just under two years. South and east they sailed, around the Cape of Good Hope and south of Australia, swinging up at last to reach Tahiti on March 6, 1797. (Actually, it seems to have been March 5th. Captain Wilson apparently forgot that in crossing the dateline from the west they had gained a day instead of dropping one. Twenty-four years later the missionary calendar at Tahiti was still one day ahead of the rest of the world.) Wilson dropped other missionaries at the Tonga Islands and the Marquesas, and the DUFF plotted a course that led through the Carolines toward the Palaus and home.

In the Carolines Wilson discovered five islands. Satawal was passed, and on October 26th the ship paused at Lamotrek, long known by name, a lovely island to the east of Ifaluk. The people welcomed them, and a Swede aboard, Andrew Lind, asked to be set ashore to stay. Wilson granted the request, leaving him with a gift of tools, knives, and a Bible. The ship sailed on, and for a century thereafter some charts of the Carolines referred to Lamotrek as "Swede Island."

They passed Elato, and the next day, on October 27, 1797, the ship found Ifaluk. Wilson never knew it, however. His chart, which listed "Iselook," was not much of an improvement over Cantova's original, and his navigation was not particularly accurate. He thought he had discovered a previously uncharted island. The published account, written from the log of the DUFF, is maddeningly brief and uninformative:

"27th. About ten A.M. we came in sight of another low island, bearing S.W. and as we altered our course to go to the southward of it, when west of us it shewed like two distinct islands, lying near each other: here also many of the natives came off, and trafficked as the others had done. One thing we had observed as peculiar and remarkable, that hitherto in our range among these islands no females had appeared; whence we concluded the men either more jealous than their eastern neighbors, or as placing a higher value on their women; or, perhaps, they had at some period suffered in defending them from licentious visitors. The latitude of these sister islands is 74°14′N. longitude 144°50′E. At four P.M. the latter bore E. by N. two leagues."

Heading westward the DUFF reached Woleai, where some sixty canoes put out to meet the ship. The people, as on Lamotrek (and presumably Ifaluk as well) were most anxious to get scraps of iron. They traded coconut rope "equal, if not superior in strength to our own hemp-made ropes" for pieces of old iron barrel-hoop. The good behavior of the people impressed Wilson, and he was amazed at the perfection of their woven skirts and loin-cloths. His account is so like our own arrival at Ifaluk a century and a half later that it makes me homesick to read it. The DUFF sailed on through the Palaus to Macao, and at last, on July 11, 1798, again cast anchor in the Thames. It was nearly thirty years before another ship left records of a stop at Ifaluk.

There were almost certainly visitors who didn't leave records; occasional whalers, and perhaps a trader or two looking for rope, pearl shell, or bêche-de-mer for the China trade. It seems likely that visits were few and brief, and that Ifaluk escaped the rape and destruction inflicted on Ponape, Kusaie, and Polynesian islands when the whaling fleets put in. There are indications that most of the contacts during this period were the result of canoe voyages by the islanders.

Clearly iron was well-known and in great demand in the western Carolines in Wilson's time, and I thought Tom and Toroman might know stories of the first coming of iron to the island. They did. The "when" of it all was impossible to get at; Toroman grunted "moshua moshua," literally "before-before," the Ifaluk equivalent of long ago, or once upon a time. Ifaluk first heard of iron from the men of neighboring islands. The wonderful material was reported to come from Guam, some 400 miles to the north.

Canoes from Ifaluk had sailed to Guam. Tom didn't know the details, though he added with some pride that he could have sailed them there himself; this was very likely true, since Tom was the ranking navigator on the atoll. They returned at length with some implements of iron, and Ifaluk retreated its first step from the Age of Shell. It was a small step, for at least a century later in 1909 it was reported that all of the adzes in use were still made of shell, though some of the drills were iron-tipped.

There are other stories of trading trips, as well, and one of the most interesting is passed to us by the naturalist-poet Adelbert von Chamisso, who accompanied the first voyage of the Russian explorer Kotzebue in the Pacific, 1815–1817. Kotzebue's ship, the RURICK, did not explore the Carolines, but on Guam Chamisso picked up information on the western Carolines from a Spaniard who had been there,

Don Luis de Torres. According to Torres, the Caroline islanders of the 1700's knew of Guam only in ancient song and legend. Then in 1788 a great canoe navigator from the Carolines, Luito by name, re-discovered the route to Guam. He arrived with two canoes, was well received by the Spaniards, departed for home, and returned again in 1789 with four canoes. He asked the Governor's permission to come annually and this was granted, but Luito's four canoes were lost on the return trip in 1789 and the trips ceased. In 1804 Torres voyaged to the Carolines and landed on Woleai. Here he discovered that the voyages had been interrupted because Luito's canoes had not returned, and the islanders suspected foul play. Torres persuaded the chief navigator of Woleai to draw him an island chart of the western Carolines, and told the people they would be welcomed on Guam. The trading voyages were resumed, on a larger scale than before. Canoes from Woleai, Satawal, and other neighboring islands (which very likely included Ifaluk) would gather yearly at Lamotrek and sail to-ward Guam in April. The voyage usually took five days; two days from Lamotrek to Fayo (West Fayu, an uninhabited island still visited by Ifalukians today), and three more days from Fayu to Guam, sailing before the wind. In 1814 the Lamotrek fleet to Guam consisted of eighteen canoes, and the islanders traded canoes, shells, and curiosities for iron, glass beads, cloth and other items.

This account provides a healthy antidote for the widespread impression that the "civilized man" always takes the initiative in trading with "backward peoples." It supports the tales told to Jesuits Clain and Cantova, a century before, of the dominant positions held by the islands of Lamotrek and Woleai, which lie on either side of Ifaluk. The fact that Guam was known to the Carolinians in song and legend but not visited suggests that contact with Guam may have been avoided during the previous century, perhaps as a result of tales of Spanish atrocities. There is no mention here, or in any earlier account, of any regular contact of the Woleai-Lamotrek group with either Yap or Ulithi, or of any influence from Yap. It is difficult to know what to make of this last. Perhaps the Yap Empire was not yet established, but the intricacy of sociological relationships within the empire suggests a body of custom which grew up over a prolonged period.

The next ship, after Wilson's, to leave an account of Ifaluk was the Russian corvette SENIAVIN, captained by Fedor Lütke under the orders of Czar Nicholas I, on a voyage around the world with stops at Russian America, Kamchatka, and Micronesia. Baron von Kittlitz, one of three naturalists travelling aboard, left a brief account of the atoll, but a more complete story of the visit is in Lütke's own narrative of the voyage, here freely translated. It was April of the year 1828:

"Having gone south to the latitude of 7°21', we then headed west. It is at this latitude that are situated the 'two islands' of Wilson, in which, after all the calculations, we have no doubt of finding the Ifalouk group, and we were not mistaken in our conjectures. We saw them on the 3rd of April. They consist, not of two, but of four little islands, namely: Ifalouk, Moay, Ella, and Fararyk, situated, as would be expected, on a reef which forms a lagoon of about five miles around. This group is relatively more populated than the others. While waiting for the wind to change, we were surrounded by twenty-five canoes full of islanders, who distinguished themselves from all other people of the Carolines by their boisterous spirits. They all wanted to come aboard the boat and it was necessary to stop them by force. They all asked for something to eat; they all offered for sale shells, woven materials and even canoes and they knew quite well how to take an advantage. They finally showed a trait for which we were all prepared after statements of Wilson and certain whale fishermen. One impudent islander seized a toggle and jumped overboard with it. At the same time the chief of the group was on board; I told him that I would keep him on the boat until the stolen object had been returned. He was quite frightened but the others remained tranquil, assuring us that the toggle would be returned immediately; and, in fact, one of the chiefs found it in one of the canoes and returned it, asking for an ax in return for the service he had rendered in getting it back. While all this was happening and while I was in the midst of trying to pacify the old chief with presents, another repeated the same trick, diving off the poop deck; but after just a few moments, through the intervention of the same chiefs, he was forced to reappear himself with the stolen toggle. I was sorely tempted to make an example of him to the others, to give him a few lashes. However, the poor devil was in such a state that I let him go and he made off quickly in his canoe for fear he would be taken again.

"We had no little difficulty in getting rid of our guests. After being rid of them, we headed west toward the 'Oulea' or 'Ouleai' (Woleai) group . . . which we saw toward evening."

Lütke's account of the "boisterous spirits" and fearless approach of the people suggests that the Ifalukians had not yet suffered at the hands of Europeans, and that visiting ships were so rare that caution, protocol, and standards of behavior for dealing with them had not yet developed. The thefts are out of character for Ifaluk today; perhaps they were atypical for Lütke's time as well, and represented sudden succumbing to temptation in the face of unimaginable wealth, fleeting opportunity, and ignorance of penalty. Lütke himself says in summary:

"On all the islands of the lower Carolines that we visited, we found the same kind of people, the same hospitality, the same good naturedness and . . . the same gaiety which characterized the people . . . The long voyages that the islanders undertook, their frequent visits to their neighbors, as well as their journeys even to the European colonies —none of these altered in any way the remarkable innocence of their morals, nor did it instill in them the desire to appropriate the goods of others in dishonest ways. One is led to believe that the 'commercial spirit' which animated them taught them at a very early age to respect in others the things which they themselves had acquired with no little difficulty, and which they have come to appreciate full well."

On the other hand, the account of Lütke's ornithologist, Kittlitz, suggests the Ifalukians were an obstreperous lot. He writes of ". . . a relatively very strong people, who distinguished themselves scarcely to their own advantage. Not only did all of them show much selfishness in trading but . . . a pair of attempts at stealing . . . confirmed the evil rumors which had already been spread about these tiny islands by the whale fishermen." If this is accurate, Ifaluk's manners toward visitors have showed a marked improvement in the last century.

Ifaluk was now on the island charts in the proper place. Lütke's figure for longitude (he gave it as 215°29'08"W., which seems like a

lot of longitude; today we would write this as 144°30′52″E.) was more
accurate than Wilson's, and anyone with a ship, a knowledge of navigation, and a good reason could sail to the spot. Few had all three, and
fewer still left records. The notorious English trader, Andrew Cheyne,
later brutally executed for rape by the Palauans, touched briefly at
Ifaluk in 1844, and reported the reefs covered with first class bêche-de-
mer (they still are today). "His Majesty" D. D. O'Keefe, an Irish-
American fabled for bringing great cartwheels of stone money from
Palau to Yap, traded in the area, and the old men remembered hearing
of his name and visits to Ifaluk. In March of 1875 the British schooner
RUPAK, on a trading voyage from Singapore, hove to at "Evalonk"
(surely a misprint for "Evalouk"). Several canoes came out, and the
ship traded tobacco for flying fish. Mr. Skinner, part owner of the
vessel, noted that the people were ". . . a tall, handsome race, of
light colour, their bodies being closely tattooed all over, their dress
being the same as that of the Ulleai (Woleai) people."

These occasional contacts amounted to very little. Ifaluk had no
particular attractions, and its very lack of isolation was a protection.
There were larger and richer islands not far away, and these drew
most of the sparse traffic in the area. In comparison with other Pacific
islands, Ifaluk was left strictly alone, and the few casual visitors left
little mark on the atoll and its people.

Meanwhile in far-off Europe, a new group began to take an interest
in the western Pacific—the Germanic merchant princes. Decades before the separate German states became a nation, German traders and
planters began to arrive in the Marshall islands, and they came to
stay. Stores were established, and forests cleared to make way for
coconut trees in ordered rows. Most of the new invaders were, or soon
became, agents of the German companies that were later to unite as
the Jaluit Gesellschaft, a branch of the Godeffroy commercial empire
in which Prince Otto von Bismarck was a stockholder. There was little
competition from other westerners, and on the larger islands the German
agents became a sort of government. Soon they extended to the Gilbert
and Ellice islands, and into the eastern Carolines.

Officially, the Carolines still belonged to Spain, but Spanish influence
in the Pacific waned with the star of the mother land. As the later half

of the 19th century progressed, German traders reached into the western Carolines, and somewhere in this period Ifaluk gained the tobacco habit. Englishmen and Japanese came as well, and at last Spain made a few half-hearted attempts to defend her interests. A Spanish gunboat put in at Woleai about 1874, hauled down the flag of an English trader, hoisted the banner of Spain, and destroyed many breadfruit and coconut trees as a punishment and warning to the people before departing. Hardly were they out of sight before the inhabitants burned the flag and killed the native pilot who had guided the Spanish crew-boat ashore. Ifaluk, less than forty miles away, heard of these things.

The Franco-Prussian War came, and after it the union of Teutonic states. And when the new nation reached for Pacific lands, it found the commercial groundwork for empire already laid. The expansion was rapid, and the Spanish Carolines were enveloped from the south and east. The Bismarck archipelago and a piece of New Guinea went to the Germans in 1884–1885; the Solomon Islands followed shortly, as did the Marshall Islands where the German trading firms had controlled things for years; still later came interests in Samoa. Inevitably activities increased in the Carolines, and at Yap the naval forces of Spain and Germany came close to blows. The dispute was arbitrated by Pope Leo XIII, who in 1885 confirmed Spain's ownership, but granted to the Germans and British free trading rights to the scattered islands. Rebellions on Yap and Ponape further added to Spain's troubles.

The end came in 1899. Following the Spanish-American War, Spain relinquished her last oceanic possessions. Guam and the Philippines went to America as spoils of war, and the Germans purchased the rest of the Marianas, the Palaus, and the Carolines for 16,810,000 marks ($4,500,000).

For Ifaluk it was not the beginning of the "Deutsch time," but it was the beginning of the most memorable part. With characteristic system and thoroughness the Germans set out to make the Pacific empire pay its way and show a profit. In the Caroline atolls the Germans were interested in order, copra, phosphates and labor. Order in a social and political sense was something Ifaluk possessed already, but to the Germans it included as well a geometrical sort of orderliness that has left its mark on Ifaluk. Yani mentioned an aspect of it casually one day as we passed a deserted house site in the forest.

"Now all people live near lagoon," he said, gesturing at the ancient foundation. "Not like before. Before, some people live everywhere. Houses not so close then. More trees in between, and no big roads."

There had been villages then, but on German decree all dwellings were concentrated at these sites. The strip of land along the lagoon shore was ordered cleared of underbrush, and kept free of trash. The lagoon trail, perhaps already present as a path, was widened, straightened, and curbed with lines of coral rocks; we should have called it "Ifalukstrasse." So it was through the Germans that the atoll gained its park-like village areas, its broad pathways, and its regular island cleanups. Not wholly free of Germanic prejudices ourselves, we thought these alterations might represent an improvement; at any rate, half a century has established them firmly in local tradition.

For a time near the turn of the century there were alien residents on Ifaluk; a European called "Sau," and one or more Japanese. At intervals German ships called by to collect copra in exchange for tobacco and a few other trade goods. And from time to time the German labor recruiters came.

Blackbirding had been a thriving business in Oceania during the 19th century, and in somewhat modified form it was to continue well toward the middle of the 20th as well. The Germans needed men for the copra plantations as far away as Samoa, and workers to mine phosphates on Fais and the Palaus. Quotas could seldom be filled by volunteers, and many were conscripted. Tom, who had worked for a while on a German schooner, remembered these recruiters as men with white skins and knotty muscles. Their methods and the reaction to them are part of an Ifaluk song, recorded and translated by Ted Burrows:

They come to the men's house
Where the people are assembled,
And seize men to take them away.

They came in the afternoon
And hunted men by night.
Nobody could sleep for fear of them.

> *In front of the men's house*
> *The Germans lined up the Caroline men.*
> *They are pleased to see so many—*
> *They have captured ten,*
> *Strong men all.*

> *"Come along! Get into the raft!"*
> *They feel the arms of the captives,*
> *And chuckle with glee*
> *To find them so strong.*
> *The first mate takes them aboard.*

At that, the Germans were probably an improvement over the earlier Pacific island exploiters and slavers, for some of the Ifaluk men who were taken away eventually reached home again. The German Colonial district agents were often educated men, and the general attitude of the government was one of farming the atolls for steady income, rather than robbing them for single profitable hauls. The agent on Yap wrote articles on the people and places he visited, and at last a full-fledged scientific expedition to the Carolines was organized.

Ernst Sarfert, a twenty-seven-year-old anthropologist with the expedition, was put ashore on Ifaluk on Nov. 5, 1909, and picked up again on Nov. 17. The notes made during his twelve-day visit form our first account of the culture of Ifaluk. They touch on many things that Burrows studied in detail later. There are a few familiar names, if I read Sarfert's phonetics correctly; Fagolier was a "grown son" then, and Maroligar a lad of five.

Sarfert arrived only two and a half years after the worst typhoon in Ifaluk's remembered history. It had hit on March 27–28, 1907, and memories of it are starkly clear today. Tom and Toroman often spoke of it. The first winds blew in from the northeast, building up to a roaring blast white with the foam of the tossing sea. Trees toppled but no lives were lost in the first pass. The winds died, and there was a lull as the eye of the storm passed over the atoll. Then they began again, and it was the later storm winds, striking furiously from the south, that spread the real destruction. The sky darkened and the rushing air struck Ifaluk like a giant fist. The sea rose in mountains. Huge waves, taller than the coconut trees, swept over Ella islet and

Falielang, ripping great blocks from the living reef and hurling them across the flats. The waves poured over Falalap, killing thirty-four villagers and leaving big sharks floundering in the bwol. Falarik suffered destruction of villages and forests, but only a single life was lost. Tom recalled with high glee that several ladies had lost their skirts in the flood. The narrative of the German expedition tells of the sight, two and a half years after the storm; many white broken trunks of strong trees extended over the low brush, and the coconut trees lay strewn in windrows on the ground. It was this storm that finally completed the union of the islet Maia with the northern end of Falarik. The atoll was recovering during Sarfert's visit, but food was short and some islanders were still sojourning on neighboring atolls.

Japanese workers entered the Carolines in increasing numbers during the German period. Many were employed by German companies, and others fished the area. It was not long before the Japanese formed the largest resident alien population in the islands. When World War I broke out, Japan was quick to relieve the Germans of their island empire; the change of ownership was sanctioned by treaty and mandate in 1921.

The next quarter century saw sweeping changes as Japan worked to develop Micronesian resources as no foreign power had done before. The greatest efforts went into the high fertile islands of the Marianas and the Carolines, but even the tiniest atolls were not wholly ignored. And slowly a palm-leaf curtain descended about the area, cutting it off from the eyes of the world.

Ifaluk saw more of the Japanese as time went on, though visits were never common. Trading ships called by for copra, and took the trouble to bring goods the people really wanted: bush knives, adze blades, red and black aniline dyes, steel fishhooks, red face paint, and a few small cotton fishnets and bits of cloth. A small store of some sort was apparently established in Rauau village, though it was opened only when Japanese vessels dropped anchor at the island. No trace of it remains today.

With the other items came the first mosquito bars. They were crude things, opaque canopies of cheap muslin that kept out the breeze along with the mosquitoes; but smothering or not, they were considered an invention to rank with the steel adze. And, as Yani once remarked, with a detached air and a studious look at the treetops, for married couples in crowded houses they had certain advantages over the transparent American nets. He glanced back at me and doubled up; deadpan humor was not his forte.

The Japanese made some attempt at providing medical care for their atoll wards. Twice, following epidemics in the 1930's, ships came to give shots and vaccinations to everyone. The shots made a great impression for they were administered by a nurse, the first woman of the outer world to be seen by most of Ifaluk. There were labor recruiters too, as in the German days, and many a middle-aged Ifaluk man has grubbed phosphate hardpan from the ground on Fais and in the Palaus. Some of the boys were taken away to a Japanese school on Yap, where they learned a bit of the new lingua franca of Micronesia. Yani and others among our friends had gone. They recalled the teacher as a severe and pompous little man who slapped their hands with rulers, but none seemed to regret the experience. Only the Yapese objected strenuously at this pampering of their inferior country cousins.

Canoe voyaging declined during the Japanese period. The new masters forbad long sailing trips, but allowed some travel on the decks of Japanese vessels. An attempt was made to increase copra production, and a young Japanese agriculturist was sent to Ifaluk to see what could be done. He supervised the clearing of part of Ella for a coconut plantation shortly before the war, but the planting was never done. From Yani's description he seems to have been a likeable extrovert. He learned to speak the language passably, fraternized freely with the young men, and generally found his way into the hearts of the people.

When war with America came the first effects were slight. Canoe travel was banned and the agriculturist removed. An airstrip was built on Woleai atoll, and occasional planes flew over. Some local wag referred to Ifaluk's ubiquitous flies as "native airplanes," and a standard island joke was born. Then Japanese visits declined and finally ceased; on the last trips many of the younger men were taken away to Yap.

The war passed Ifaluk by. There was a single strafing run by an

American Navy pilot who probably thought he was shooting at Woleai. Nobody was hurt, but it nearly scared the loin-cloth off the portly Wolpaitik, who happened to be tending a fish trap in the lagoon at the time. The men who had gone away were missed, but America remained a vague name for a mighty far-off land.

Yap was a different story. For the Carolinians here America was soaring planes and bursting bombs. The men were forced to build dugouts, fill holes in airstrips, and scrounge for their own food, but they seem not to resent this now. The Japanese masters worked hard and often went hungry too. A few Ifaluk men were killed by American bombs and bullets; this too is accepted without bitterness. I think they realized clearly that they were pigmy bystanders, trapped on a battlefield where careless giants fought. The idea of wars they could understand, for Ifaluk had fought its own bloody battles in the past, and the warrior chief Mailias was its greatest hero in traditional song. The scope and power of the war, the reasons for it—these were beyond them, incomprehensible. Doubtless many of our own fighting men never saw the war in full perspective, either.

At last it was over. The end of the war marked the beginning of a new period in Ifaluk history, the " 'Merican time." The victorious Navy came in great ships and repatriated the men from Yap. Yani's main recollection of the trip back was the incredible array of foods on the vessel after months of near starvation. It was good to be home again, and the island rejoiced. New ships came, bringing a flag to Ifaluk, rounds of shots for everyone, the beginnings of a new trade, and a piece of paper telling of the new overlord and carrying hope of better times to come.

CHAPTER XIV

FISHES AND LIZARDS

I CROSSED off another day and flipped the pages on the calendar Ted Burrows had thoughtfully tacked in a conspicuous place on the tall centerpost in the Fan Nap, back in the "before-before." Ifaluk might seem a timeless land, but there were the little squares, neatly boxing the weeks and days remaining. Informally we took stock of the expedition's work, asking ourselves again, "What are we trying to do? What have we found out? How can we best spend the time left?"

The human natural history part of the project seemed fairly well in hand, all things considered. Yani and I continued to keep track of the amount and type of food consumed by selected families and to record the take in communal fish catches, but the bulk of this sort of work was done. The land environment, too, had received its share of study; here the ubiquitous lizards and land crabs seemed the most neglected items and we marked them for a further look. The sea? Here the problems seemed endless. We had spent a good many days exploring the lagoon, tramping the reefs, studying selected profiles, photographing and tabulating associations, collecting and counting organisms, recording food habits and the like. It seemed a bare descriptive start.

From any standpoint the fishes were going to loom important. I had approached them myself from the standpoint of food. Fishes were eaten by man and other organisms. In turn, the fishes ate other things —smaller fishes, invertebrates, plankton, seaweeds, and miscellaneous detritus. The records of this sort were very far from complete, and by themselves gave only a fragmentary insight into Ifaluk's submarine world of fins and scales. Moreover, I was not trained, equipped, or inclined to handle the rest of it. What had been needed was a real ichthyologist, and now in Bob Rofen we had a fine one.

I feel sorry for the man who isn't wholeheartedly devoted to at least one thing in the realm of man or nature, be it lovely ladies, sea urchins, politics, or stamps. Bob Rofen had a passion all right, and it was for fishes. Not fish, for to the partisan ichthyologist "fish" is singular, or plural only for a group of one species; more than one kind is always "fishes."

Bob had taken his doctorate at Stanford University, a center for the study of fishes since the days of its first President, David Starr Jordan. Now Bob helped direct the newly established George Vanderbilt Foundation, with headquarters there. Bob's project was to get specimens and information on fishes, and to cooperate with the rest of us in more general objectives. Foremost in his mind was a clear image of a treatise, extending to several volumes, on the fishes of the tropical western Pacific, with every species well described and illustrated in color.

In some ways this objective was easier to put across to Ifaluk than some of the others we had in mind. One day soon after his arrival Bob hauled out a large volume on the sea fishes of South Africa. He opened it while local friends and bystanders clustered about, and carefully explained his project.

The young men turned the pages carefully, fascinated by the colored plates. Excitedly they identified familiar species, and exclaimed over kinds they had never seen. Would Ifaluk help get material for a set of books like this? It most certainly would, for Ifaluk, like Bob, had fish (or fishes) on its collective mind much of the time.

If it is possible for an ichthyologist to come loaded for bear, Bob had done so. His mountain of equipment dwarfed Ted Bayer's and mine together, for modern fish collecting is a large scale business, no job for a Sunday Isaac Walton. In his arsenal was nearly every gadget that the fertile mind of man had devised through the millennia to outwit the fish and snare him for the platter.

There were hooks, of course, for everything from minnows to sharks, and lines ranging from nylon threads to heavy cod-line. Nets of all kinds, too, though none so impressive as the great seines of Ifaluk that were sometimes linked in lengths of half a mile.

Then came the spears. Simple Hawaiian sling spears, driven by a slingshot through a hollow tube. French Arbalete spear guns, whose tense rubber cables had the pull of an English longbow drawn to the ear. Then a lethal weapon that hurled its shaft with pressurized CO_2. There were excited comments and predatory gleams as Bob casually dropped the word that those who helped him could learn to use these weapons.

Last, and certainly the most effective bolt in Rofen's arsenal, was the fish poison rotenone. Looking over the lot it seemed the only things missing were fish trawls and dynamite. No question about it, I thought: when it came to weapons the West had it all over the so-called "savage." The meanest, most dangerous animal on earth is civilized man. Wholesale piscicide seemed in the immediate offing for Ifaluk, but this vision proved quite wrong. I had forgotten that fishes have been getting away from fishermen for a long time, too.

Collected fishes must be decently embalmed and coffined for science, and Bob's gear included things for this, too. Formaldehyde, cases of tin cans and a canning machine, big steel drums, and an acre of cheesecloth for wrapping specimens. Ted Bayer and I had brought some of these things ourselves. An aqualung with compressed air tanks was in the pile, along with tools, folding tables, and a small library on Pacific fishes. Finally, one (and only one) comfortable camp chair. Too late for me, anyway; I had developed some quite simian callosities from my evenings spent perched on an up-ended C-ration carton.

Maroligar assigned Bob a team of fishermen. Bakal, who had picked up an amazing amount of English around the Fan Nap, became a charter member. His old job of handyman was passed to young Tachiweligar, who had haunted the Fan Nap area since Marston had effectively doctored a nasty gash in the sole of his foot. Tachi was much better on the pots and pans than Bakal had ever been. Along with Bakal came Tachim, a neighbor from Soumat household and a comrade of long standing. The third fisherman was Tewas, short for Tewajiliaro, a tall, fair-skinned young man from Falalap islet. Bob

and the men worked well together; seeing them in the field one got
the impression of hilarious and frantic but well-organized activity, and
it was hard to tell where work left off and fun began.

Bob's first big fish-poisoning operation was carried out on the windward reef, just across Falarik islet from home. Yani and I were at
work already that morning, plotting the distribution of seaweeds along
a marked line extending from the shoreline out to the breakers. We
looked up as Bob and his crew trooped through the dark green
Scaevola scrub and continued down the beach, cans clinking and dipnets swinging. Half way out on the reef flat they halted. The water
was only inches deep here now, for the tide was ebbing.

Bob mixed the rotenone, adding a bit of water to the dry, brownish
powder and kneading it into a doughy mass. The men scattered this
in small lumps over a section of the outer reef flat, and stood back
to watch the cloudy waters.

Rotenone comes from the roots of the *Derris* and other plants, and
has long been used as a fish and insect poison by native peoples.
Modern technology has only refined the stuff a bit. In fishes the poison
causes constriction of the small capillary blood vessels in the gills,
preventing free blood flow in the region where respiration normally
takes place. As the animals suffocate they come to the surface, gasping
for air and alternately drifting and darting erratically about. Dying,
they float at the top or drift with currents along the bottom.

The poison acted fairly swiftly. Within minutes Bob and his men
were chasing about with excited shouts and laughter, scooping up the
floundering fishes. The noise attracted other islanders; they came,
watched, and joined in the hunt. Soon there were twenty people
splashing in the shallows, chasing fishes and adding them to the cans.

Watching them, Yani began to get restless. A gaudy parrotfish, half
stupefied, charged recklessly past us and cut out over the reef edge.
Yani swiped at it with our bucket as it went by. Then, as the poison
spread, the small fishes in our area began flopping about, too. It seemed
a shame that they should die in vain, and soon we were chasing and
scooping up fishes with the rest.

We headed for a deeper pool on the reef flat, and commenced turning over dead coral blocks to get the fishes trapped below. Small goat-

fishes with whisker-like barbels below the chin littered the bottom, in company with more brightly colored species. One uplifted rock yielded a sizeable brown moray eel. It darted out, then recoiled in a sinuous posture, head drawn back and needle teeth gleaming in its opened mouth. We left him for a later time. Our bucket was filling, and we went to dump it into one of Bob's larger cans. As we arrived, Toroman came up with a delighted smile and added a double handfull of small fishes to the pot.

In the end the cans were filled to overflowing with fishes, drab and brilliant. Bob was pleased with the size and variety of the catch. Ifaluk was pleased, too; for Bob had set aside a pile of surplus common species as food for those who had helped. I was pleased myself, for the invertebrates in the poisoned area didn't seem much affected, and the region should soon recover from this rather selective removal of organisms.

Bob's helpers were already expert fishermen. With startling rapidity they became experts at the other jobs that needed doing—preserving the fish, mixing fuel and running the outboard. I still carry a picture of Bakal reclining in the speeding boat, chin cupped in both hands, steering and operating the motor controls with his prehensile toes. Eventually the men took the WAT on many trips by themselves while Bob stayed home, sorting, identifying, labeling, and packing the growing collection. On trips alone they always chose an area that would yield meat fishes along with the rare oddities that particularly pleased Bob.

Not that oddities, at least things that looked odd to me, were at all rare; the reefs seemed loaded with them. Some, like the parrotfishes and wrasses with beak-like teeth for nibbling corals and algae, and the long-nosed butterfly fishes, ran to extremes in gaudy colors and disruptive patterns. Other fishes had unlikely shapes. There were blood-red worm eels with two-foot bodies no thicker than a pencil, burrowed deeply in the sand; thin needle-fish with pointed beaks; and blocky little frog-fishes with leg-like fins modified for creeping about in protected places. Still other fishes appeared well-defended. The surgeon fishes had small sharp bones near the base of the tail which could be protruded suddenly like switchblade knives. There were puffers that bloated their bodies into spiny globes. The plump, slow, trigger fishes, like the Bwup (*Pseudobalistes flavimarginatus*), had a large dorsal spine that could be raised and locked in place, allowing the animals to jam themselves inextricably in reef crevices.

Among the oddest fishes were those that lived inside other animals —sea cucumbers, for example. The giant cucumber *Thelenota*, like lots of its relatives, uses its hind-intestine for a sort of breathing. Muscles pump water into the anus and hindgut, and thence to a pair of complex respiratory tubes where it is held and then expelled in a sudden stream. The whole system acts as a water lung, inhaling and exhaling the sea. The continual series of high clysters keeps the hindgut flushed and clean, and a slender fish (*Jordanicus*) lives within this pulsing cave, coming out periodically to feed.

Ted Bayer turned up another fish living in the starfish *Culcita novaeguineae*. The latter were fat, nearly armless animals, more like pentagonal pillows than sea-stars. Ted had collected several, and as he cut the first one open to drain the body fluid, a plump, pale fish (*Carapus*) slid out the opening. Ted had seen the things before, in *Culcita* from New Guinea, but Rofen went wild when he saw it. The rest of Ted's starfishes were immediately hacked open. Some contained fish, and these were carefully preserved for the collection.

Close physical relationships of this sort between unlike species never failed to intrigue us, and at this point it would have been very easy to drop some of our more grandiose plans and investigate in detail the natural history of this fish. What did it eat? Did it go in and out of the sea star, and if so, how? How and at what stage of life did it enter in the first place? With one fish to a sea star, how did it reproduce? We never learned.

As a group, the bony fishes provide a beautiful example of what biologists call "adaptive radiation." The descendants of the ancient ancestral stock of the bony fishes have slowly diversified and invaded a variety of environments, evolving adaptations to many different ways of life. The result of this fan-wise spread in space and time is a great host of species of varied sizes, shapes, colors, and other adaptive specializations. In the matter of food, for example, there are carnivores of many sorts, some with sharp teeth for handling other fishes and

LEFT The people dug a series of elegant wells so that Arnow could study the fresh water lens.

BELOW Water profile chart BY ABBOTT

BOTTOM The outer margin of the reef, exposed at low tide, was made up of a great variety of different kinds of organisms.

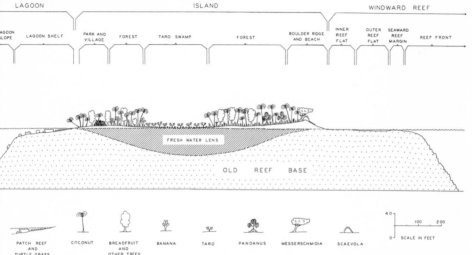

LAGOON   ISLAND   WINDWARD REEF

LAGOON SLOPE   LAGOON SHELF   PARK AND VILLAGE   FOREST   TARO SWAMP   FOREST   BOULDER RIDGE AND BEACH   INNER REEF FLAT   OUTER REEF FLAT   SEAWARD REEF MARGIN   REEF FRONT

FRESH WATER LENS

OLD REEF BASE

PATCH REEF AND TURTLE GRASS   COCONUT   BREADFRUIT AND OTHER TREES   BANANA   TARO   PANDANUS   MESSERSCHMIDIA   SCAEVOLA

40
0   100   200   SCALE IN FEET

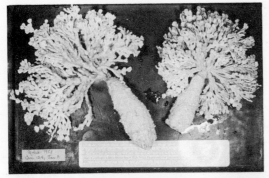

LEFT *Halimeda stuposa*, a common alga of the sandy bottom of the lagoon.

BELOW Large, nearly armless starfish, *Culcita novaeguineae*.
PHOTO BY HARRY

LEFT The monitor lizard, *Varanus indicus*.

BELOW Giant sea cucumbers, *Thelenota ananas*.

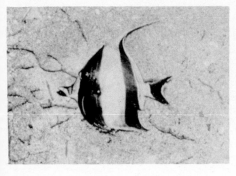

ABOVE "Liwaisola," *Zanclus cornutus.*

TOP RIGHT "Taguruatr," *Gnathodentex aurolineatus.*

RIGHT A parrot fish, "rou," *Scarus microrhinus.*

RIGHT Gavileisei with a coconut crab.

BELOW A large hermit crab.

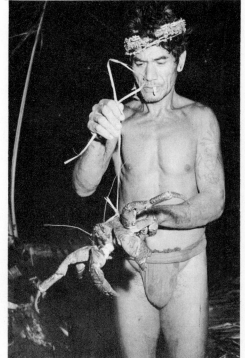

ABOVE There was a stone fish weir in the pass between Falalap and **Falarik.**

BELOW Marston—all ready to go out after a picture.

softer invertebrates, others with blunt plates for crushing molluscs and coral. Some fishes are equipped with fine, bristle-like strainers on the gills for filtering plankton from the sea. Other species feed on plant material or detritus, and are suitably equipped for this. Specific adaptations to specific food habits seem endless. Similarly with habitat; some fishes burrow, some lie on the bottom, and some lurk in crevices of rock and reef. A host of others swim more or less freely in the water, each form tending to remain within some more or less restricted region and type of environment.

Each of these many species is in varying degree specifically adapted to its own individual ecological niche—a particular way of life under a pretty specific range of conditions. Such specialization has its rewards in greater capacity for survival under the specified conditions, but it has its dangers, too. Species too specialized to face much change are candidates for early extinction if their environments are altered. Survival, here as elsewhere, requires a jittery sort of balance between specialization and flexibility.

Most of the fishes Bob had taken thus far had been relatively small. True, a few young sharks had wandered into the gill-net, but I kept hoping he would get something too big to stuff into one of his fifty-five gallon drums. It wasn't a matter of sport or science but of seeing what Bob would do with such a fish, once he had it. Big fish were certainly around. We had spotted some in the ship pass and others beyond the reefs. And we had heard stories of the big Taiyau, told by Yani while Ted Arnow was still with us.

Arnow had started things one night with a story of a fish with a mouth that could hold a man—well, half a man, anyway. There were legends of such fish on Pacific islands from Tahiti to the East Indies, and Arnow had made a point of collecting them. The fish wasn't a shark, but a big grouper with a bulldog head. Bob was pretty sure the yarns referred to giant specimens of the sea bass *Epinephelus lanceolatus,* or something closely related.

Yani was there with us, and he spoke up. Ifaluk had such stories he said. What was more, the fish was here, too. He recalled that he and I had seen a small one only a yard long in the ship pass the day we had observed the tidal currents. On Ifaluk it was called the

Taiyau, and most specimens seen were quite harmless. Not all, however. The atoll boasted at least one monster with a mouth two feet across. Yani and many of the other men had seen it from time to time.

Here was Arnow's yarn coming to life. We listened fascinated as Yani went on.

The big Taiyau lived outside the reef ridge south of tiny Elangalap islet, where the reef front dropped abruptly in a great submarine cliff. There were gloomy caves in the face of the cliff, and here the Taiyau lurked.

It wasn't a fierce fish like the sharks, Yani said. Usually it swam slowly or lingered nearly motionless at the mouth of its cavern home. Sometimes it emerged majestically to investigate something in its neighborhood. Ordinarily it didn't bother people. Not that anyone went out of the way to give it much chance.

What made people leery, Yani went on, was the size of the animal and especially of its mouth, for when the mouth opened, things in the near vicinity were simply sucked in. A group of fishermen off Elangalap had seen the fish open its mouth and inhale a smallish sea turtle one day, and the turtle hadn't come out. No one on Ifaluk had been inhaled, but there were these stories from other islands, and men certainly recognized the possibility. Even a slow fish might be dangerous to an unwary swimmer if it got big enough and curious enough.

Not many days after this, Tom came by to warn us that a big Taiyau was now in the lagoon. This was unusual; generally such fish stayed outside the reef, but several fishermen had seen the beast on trips across the lagoon. It had come up slowly from near the bottom as a great dark shadow fatter than a shark. It had nosed near the surface and retreated again, apparently deciding that canoes were not suitable for dinner. The lagoon fishermen were a bit more cautious now, staying in their canoes or keeping extra close to them while swimming over the deeper water.

Two days later I looked up from the deep patch reef from which I was collecting coral-boring organisms to find a monstrous fish investigating me. To this day I recall the animal as about the size of a barn door, though water magnifies things about a third, and imagination often much more than that. I nearly lost my pants getting ashore. A look in Bob's fish books showed it was probably a giant parrot fish, with a high bulging forehead. These animals get over six feet long and run to several hundred pounds, but are quite harmless.

With collecting trips nearly every favorable day the fishes flowed into Bob's cans in a fairly steady stream, and it looked as though the list of species might eventually reach 400 for the atoll. Bob and the team took most of these, but others helped too. Knowing that Bob wanted at least one of everything, and that he already had the commoner things, the men of the villages began to bring in any unusual fishes taken on their own private fishing trips. Too, Bob showed visitors to the Fan Nap colored pictures of the things he wanted most, and men went out deliberately to get them if the animals were known to occur in Ifaluk waters. Some of the rarer butterfly and parrot fishes were taken practically on order. Tawaitiu, a young man from Falitrel household, Falalap, was a master at locating rare fish. I wondered how many biologists at home knew the natural history of their own backyards well enough to do this sort of collecting if called upon. Bob always paid for desired specimens with tobacco, fish hooks, or money, but I suspect the rewards that pleased the fishermen most were Bob's excited shouts when something new and rare came along. It gave them a certain added social prestige in a culture where such status was not easily attained.

Collecting "on order" worked well enough with the fishes to encourage us to try the same thing with the lizards. And thinking about lizards reminded me of Marston. Not that the two resembled each other, much anyway, but associations are unpredictable things. My thoughts went back to a conversation of some two months earlier. It had started with the subject of wives.

Ten P.M. in the old laboratory, under the tent fly. The day's notes had been completed and lay in a pile on the crate that served as a desk. The Coleman lantern shed a bright island of light within the microcosm of the big white mosquito bar. A faint breeze stole through the net, shattering a plume of smoke from the tin can ashtray. With it came the sounds of the night; a whisper of restless palm fronds, the half-stilled thunder of surf on distant reefs, the dull thump of a falling coconut. I leaned back from the typewriter, thinking idly how nice it would be to go barefooted and shirtless always.

"I wish Izzie were here now." The opener was a verbal reflex.

Affirmative grunt from Marston. "Nancy, too."

So far so good. It wasn't often that a good subject for argument arose in the first sentence. Anyway, on the subject of wives we were agreed. Each of us had picked a paragon. Or had been picked. Neither of us was quite sure, and this uncertainty had been explored at length on an earlier occasion.

Tonight we got off on how the absent ladies would have fitted in with the local environment and customs. We were sure, at first, on the obvious things. Both liked tropics and informality; neither was dependent on bridge clubs and the bright lights; both would soon have been on neighborly terms with Ifaluk's women. Marston pointed out that our wives could have collected all kinds of lore on the local woman's world that was shut off from us, and even from anthropologist Ted. We were all ready to write the Pacific Science Board to ship two wives on the next plane.

Then we began to have a few doubts. Would our atoll paradise hold flaws for them, as it did for us? How about the horde of flies and mosquitoes? We decided our wives could get used to them, as we had. The rather open and public sanitary facilities? Marston felt this might not be too serious a drawback; I wasn't nearly so certain. Woman's dress on Ifaluk? I felt sure that in a couple of weeks Izzie would be sufficiently acculturated to adopt Ifaluk's topless garments; after all, there were all her Hawaiian ancestors with names like Kamoku-kaiueohopoe and Nakiloliiliiokalola. Marston had some serious doubts about Nancy. (Months later we raised this question with our wives, and enjoyed hearing the business discussed from the other side.)

There seemed no insuperable difficulties yet, though we both felt that Nancy and Izzie would disapprove of the somewhat lowly status of Ifaluk's women, and might well sow the seeds for a household revolution. There was probably some latent suffragette material here, and the picture of Ifaluk's stalwart males demoted to agricultural labor in the steaming bwol while the women took their ease in the shade of canoe houses was downright depressing.

Then I thought of the lizards. Izzie was a trained biologist, and had no qualms about octopusses and slugs, or the crawliest of bugs and spiders. But she was one of those souls to whom the reptilian world was a sort of chamber of horrors, best viewed, if this was necessary, through thick glass in a zoo. Maybe, after all, things were better off as they were.

For the lizards were everywhere on Ifaluk—in the houses, on the trees, racing through the vegetation and litter on the ground, and even occasionally venturing out on the exposed reef flats at low tide.

Most conspicuous were the big gray-green monitor lizards (*Varanus indicus*), some of them five feet long counting the whip-like tail. They were not native to the island, but had been introduced from Yap or the Palaus by the Japanese to control the rat population, and perhaps as a potential food. At any rate, they caught rats, by creeping up on them stealthily and then making a final dash and lunge. The older men felt the monitor was doing a fair job of rat control, for in the German times the rats had been much more numerous and destructive of coconuts and thatched roofs. Knowing the dense rat population on Ella islet, where the monitor was rare, I could well believe this.

Nor did the monitors confine themselves to rats. Land crabs and hermit crabs, other lizards, and even the smaller coconut crabs went down with fine impartiality. Birds, too, according to Yani, though I never saw this myself. That monitors were excellent tree climbers, we knew; in the forest they usually scurried as we came by, running over rocks and fallen logs and rattling quickly up the trunks of coconut palms. Yani said they often lurked motionless among the palm fronds until a bird lit close by. A sudden lunge and snap was enough, for over short distances the big lizards could strike like lightning.

Informants added other observations. Yani had watched occasional monitors swim across the channel between Falarik and Falalap islets, and they sometimes prowled near the edges of the reef flat at low tide. Tom swore he had seen one locate a small moray eel in a shallow pool, turn and dangle its tail in the water, wait for a bite, and whip suddenly around, tossing the eel out on the dry flats where it was pounced on and eaten. I noted this down to be checked later with other people; it recalled an American Indian legend of how the grizzly bear got its short tail. This particular monitor story turned out to be a well-known part of Ifaluk's nature folklore, much of which was accurate. Only Tom claimed to have seen it himself, and perhaps he had.

The most abundant lizards on the atoll were the blue-tailed skinks (*Emoia cyanura*). These small, dark, smoothly-polished and golden striped creatures were literally everywhere, racing across pathways and wriggling into crevices and ground litter whenever we approached. The tails of some were a gorgeous and improbable blue. The animals were wary and fast, and it seemed impossible to take them unawares. With good reason, too, we found; the lower eyelid bears a small transparent window in the center, allowing *Emoia* to see tolerably well with its eyes shut tight. A fair number of skinks have evolved similar methods of protecting their eyes without loss of vision while burrowing.

The other common species of skinks we called the palm skinks (*Dasia smaragdina*), for we nearly always found them clinging head downward on the boles of coconut palms, a few feet above the ground, their heads alert and noses stuck out at right angles to the trunk. They, too, were handsome things, nearly a foot long, with dark smooth backs and gray bellies. None of us had much luck at catching them. If we dashed at them, swinging a net (good herpetologists will shudder), they simply ran up the trunk out of reach. The slow, stalking approach usually failed, too, probably because we lacked the patience of good hunters. And the palm skinks had a well-developed knack of cautiously circling the tree, keeping the trunk between a would-be catcher and themselves.

The final lizard inhabitants of the atoll were the attractive rough-skinned geckos, which prowled about in the evening after lamps were lit, when the insects began to gather. A big species, *Gehyra oceanica*, often came down from the ceiling to sit on our suspended bunches of bananas, eating both fruit and the small fruit flies that hovered around. Smaller geckos (*Lepidodactylus lugubris*) were also regular night visitors of rafters and work tables, where they stalked and snapped up insects like pigmy versions of the monitor. Their little clicking calls were a familiar part of the background noise on quiet evenings after the typewriter was stilled.

After our fiascos at lizard catching, Marston and I had tried to persuade the children to collect them for us. No luck. There were no local taboos against taking them (we tried to respect such things); it seemed the kids just weren't interested.

Now, weeks later, we tried again, this time with a sizeable bribe in mind. Our chore-boy, Tachi, not long from the ranks of the children himself, thought a couple of pairs of Hawaiian underwater goggles would do the trick. This was a prize that would have attracted adults, too, but we had very few goggles left and we wanted a small army of children working.

Tachi rounded up a group of the kids from Rauau village and brought them to the Fan Nap. We held up the goggles while he explained the deal. The goggles were not just for one person, but for everyone in the group, to be traded around in turns. The kids were fired up immediately, and communal ownership of the goggles appeared to be no drawback. Tachi went on about the lizards; we wanted lots of all kinds, and we wanted them in good shape, preferably still with tails attached. We wouldn't take animals bashed to a fare-thee-well with rocks or clubs. They understood this, too; at least the older ones did. Tachi sent them off, and the group swelled like magic as excited young voices spread the news about the goggles.

The lizards never had a chance. Natural selection had fitted them to meet the ordinary hazards of saurian existence, but it hadn't prepared them for anything like this. We watched the children for a few minutes before we went to ready the jars for what was obviously going to be a deluge of specimens. There was the direct frontal approach of the youngest tots; a hilarious, noisy attempt to run the animals down on the ground. With a circle of four or five after the same creature this was more effective than it sounds, and it looked like fun for everyone except the lizard involved. The older kids began with the cautious approach and the sudden grab, the monitor method. Then it was discovered that small lizards could be stunned without serious injury with a sudden swipe by a palm frond.

The highest refinement that developed was the noose technique. The children made little running nooses out of grass or palm leaflets. Creeping quietly up they would drape these over the heads of unsuspecting lizards; a quick pull, and the noose closed just behind the head, capturing a struggling animal. This surprised us no end, for this was precisely the technique used by kids and herpetologists at home, yet none of us had used this method here, or had made any suggestions for its use. Further, we didn't believe any herpetologist had ever collected on Ifaluk before. It looked as though immediate necessity had mothered an invention, though we couldn't be sure.

Anyway, the technique worked as well here as in America, and nearly forty of the big palm skinks had been added to the collection before noon, along with a good lot of blue-tailed skinks. Geckos came in more slowly, for these were not often about in the daytime. Several of those taken had lost their tails, which lowered their usefulness as specimens, but we took them all. It proved impossible to refuse a smiling face and a grubby little hand holding proudly aloft a tailless lizard of any sort. Before long, one of the older boys came in with a monitor. It dangled by the neck from a noose of thin coconut cord fastened to the end of a long pole. It looked quiet enough then, but getting it safely into a container involved quite a struggle.

The day wore on, and soon we had a fine series of lizards. While youthful enthusiasm was still running high we diverted the collecting efforts to other things, suggesting this time such ground crawlers as the centipedes, millepeds, spiders, sow bugs, and beetles. Again the children delivered the goods. Among other things they unearthed a fair-sized hairy spider of the general trapdoor sort, that none of us had seen before.

When the jars were full, we called things to a halt. The two pairs of goggles were presented, and with excited shouts the children's army rushed down to the lagoon to try them out. The collecting venture had been successful quite beyond our hopes, and had taken far less time than we had expected. Specialists might find the collecting data a bit vague as to exact locality and collector, but one can't have everything. We finished the work of killing, preserving, and labeling, and went for a swim ourselves.

CHAPTER XV

THE REEFS

Looking back on things, I could see that Marston had a large and complex mind. It was wide open to new ideas and it had a knack of putting old things together in new and original ways. It was broad, too; broad enough, it sometimes seemed, to harbor at least two conflicting points of view on the same subject at the same time. And it contained a small but carefully nurtured hoard of personal prejudices.

Other people's prejudices are always interesting. Marston's list began with the dogma that all starchy foods (except possibly rice) were dull peasant fare. He stoutly defended the tomato as queen of the vegetable world, and frowned on boiled plantains as the nadir of dietary decadence.

Not that the list stopped with food. Marston was convinced that in warm climates a sensible fellow has nothing whatever to do with underwear, socks, or soap, and I must say that in this matter he made partial converts of the rest of us. Above all else, he believed that the only really suitable and civilized environments for man lay in the tropics. It had been a recurring thesis in his book *Where Winter Never Comes*. As a specialized subdivision of this last view, he held that no biologist could consider himself fully educated until he had worked in a tropical rain forest.

The rest of us had our own personal prejudices, no doubt; at least my other colleagues did. My own convictions always seemed a shade too reasonable to class as mere prejudices, such as my dislike of eggplant, tapioca, neckties, and shoes. And, of course, my feeling that no

biologist ought to consider himself fully educated until he had pot-
tered about on a coral reef.

It was on the business of rain forests and reefs that Marston's prejudices and my sound instincts came close to coinciding. Our minds
proved sufficiently flexible to come round to the view that coral reefs
are really something like underwater tropical rain forests. Both are
vast, complex, three-dimensional communities containing many and diverse species.

This brought us practically to an agreement that the proper study of
mankind is coral reefs.

The Pacific Science Board, under Harold Coolidge, had arrived at a
somewhat similar conclusion, possibly by a less devious train of
thought. As a result the Board had established the Coral Atoll Research Program, of which the Ifaluk study was a part. True, the program wasn't aimed at reef research alone, but after all, we could argue,
where would atolls be if it weren't for reefs?

Where indeed? For fundamentally, an atoll *is* a reef.

It is easy to say this; it is quite another thing to really absorb the
idea. We had been aware, long before crossing the Pacific, that Ifaluk
was a sub-circular reef bearing coral islets here and there. Somehow,
after our landing on the atoll, we managed to reverse this picture, and
during the early weeks of work on land we thought of Ifaluk as a semicircle of islands surrounded by a reef. It was the point of view of a
land animal, and it stuck with us until our first trip to the bare reef at
the north end of the atoll.

It had been a sunny Sunday, early in July. The tide was ebbing,
and the three of us, Ted Burrows, Marston, and I, had decided to
spend the day seeing how the underwater half lived on Ifaluk. We
strolled northward to the end of the lagoon pathway, then followed
the beach to the northwestern tip of Falarik islet. There, beyond the
scrubby thicket of *Scaevola*, the islet ended in a narrow strip of sand.
We walked out on the reef flat, exposed now at low tide.

It was a new world to us then, and an entrancing one, full of unexpected things. We poked among the boulders and shallow residual
pools of the reef flat near shore, disturbing black sea cucumbers and
speckled moray eels. We wandered over the algal mat of the outer

reef flat and entered, at last, the pastel world of the reef ridge. At its outer rim the surf broke gently.

On all of Ifaluk there had been no vistas except along the shore. The land was a forest, and within it the trees confined attention to things close at hand. We were like forest creatures emerging on the plains, adjusting to distances and getting our first impressions of the vastness of the world. There was space here, all about us, and a sense of freedom; the eye and mind were beckoned outward to the line where sea and sky were welded in a perfect seam.

There, at the northwestern limits of the atoll, we turned and looked back.

All of Ifaluk spread there before us. At its center lay the lagoon, a pool of blue serenity; beyond it lay Ella, a low strip of emerald. To the southeast the larger islets stretched in a great windward barrier. Turning toward the east we could see the windward reefs and both coasts of the northern tip of Falarik. And sweeping away from us in a gigantic arc to the southwest lay the curve of the leeward reef, bare of islets except for tiny Elangalap.

We stood and looked, first to one side, then the other, then back again. There it was, a ring of reef, about the same width on either side. To the windward the ring bore islets on . . . well, on the reef flat, really. To the leeward the corresponding region of the flat was broad and empty.

Marston gave a surprised exclamation: "Why the islets are just incidents on the reef!"

And so they were; just piles of sand and coral, the rubble of the reef, swept inward by a broom of wind and wave, deposited on the flats where the force that carried it was spent. Here, in a shallow heap, it formed the land. This was no new idea, but Marston had put it well, I thought. The reef was the real Ifaluk; the islets that were the homes of men were—just incidents on the reef.

In the weeks that followed, Marston and I had given priority to studies on land, but the few days of good low tides every two weeks saw us out on the reefs. We worked out the major zones across the shallow regions; we tramped around the shores of Falarik and Falalap and visited the western reef, checking variations of these zones; and

finally we selected a series of representative areas for further work. At
the first of these, on windward Falarik close to home, we established a
base line across the reef perpendicular to shore, and along this line
began a survey.

From the beginning it was the seaward margin of the reef, a strip
some twenty yards wide near the offshore end of our survey line, that
intrigued us most. Here the reef lifted in a shallow ridge; out beyond
it lay the open sea.

To Ifaluk this was the place of breakers, the line where waves in
endless ranks reared up, hurled themselves on the crest of the reef,
burst thunderously to liquid tatters, and reunited in a sheet of whis-
pering foam. To the landsman this was where the reef ended; to the
sailor it was where the reef began. Actually, it was neither, for a rich
part of the living reef lay out beyond the breakers, in the quieter
depths a few fathoms down.

The ridge was accessible only at the lowest tides, and as the water
level dropped the reef showed its teeth. Half the surface of the rise
bristled with lumps and knobs, castles and pinnacles of a dozen pastel
shades. The bulk of the living material here was pink coralline algae;
the branched heads of *Porolithon gardineri,* whose friable skeletons
withstood the waves but crunched easily underfoot, and the smoother,
tougher crusts and knobs of *Porolithon onkodes.* Below these, and often
encrusted by them, were red colonies of the organ pipe coral with
delicate gray polyps, and scattered, stunted heads of the branched
corals *Pocillopora* and *Acropora.* Ornamenting everything were tufts
of softer algae, red and green.

Compared with the algal ridges on some of the larger atolls like
Bikini, the ridge on Ifaluk was relatively undeveloped, but without
standards for comparison then it looked rich to our eyes. And at that,
only a fraction of the life here showed at the surface. Within the gal-
leried castles of coral and coralline there dwelled a swarm of living
things protected from the surf; small crabs, mantis and snapping
shrimps, colorful worms, anemones, sponges, brittle stars, sea urchins,
and the like. Getting at these things required careful work with geology pick, cold chisel, and forceps.

Toward the outer reaches of the algal ridge the bottom smoothed itself a bit and sloped gently downward into the open sea. Here in disordered ranks and phalanxes, an army of large purple sea urchins (*Heterocentrotus trigonarius*) braced itself against the onslaught of the sea, pencil-thick spines spread in a formidable array. The thought of being tumbled by the breakers over regions where these beasts averaged six to the square yard was not a pleasant one. A bare patch of rock around each animal showed where it had cropped the reef of algae with its complex, five-toothed jaws. Scattered rugs of gray sponge, some of them six yards across, covered the smoothest parts of the bottom. And at intervals in this region, deep surge channels cut the ridge transversely, providing outflow gutters for the flood of water poured onto the reef flat by the waves. Branched corals crusted the walls of these channels, along with the green knobs and upright plates of the hydrocoral *Millepora*.

All in all, the reef ridge wasn't a place designed for bare feet. Men crossed the ridge on fishing trips, and sometimes hunted here for lobsters and sea urchins, but walking was no pleasure, and people watched carefully where they put their feet. We had extra reef shoes, but only Bakal among our local collaborators could squeeze his feet into any of them.

Between the ridge and the shore lay the more monotonous plain of the reef flat, with outer and inner regions recognizable in most places. The outer flat, a shallow trough some sixty yards across, was always submerged, even at low tide. The smooth bottom here was coated by a thin mat of algae, mostly green species of *Caulerpa*, encrusted thickly with the little brown shells of the protozoan *Calcarina*. Here and there on the flat lay prostrate, wheel-shaped colonies of the massive coral *Porites*.

The inner reef flat extended from here to shore. Much of its hard surface was hidden beneath a coarse plush of the seaweed *Halimeda opuntia* which held the sand, harbored a rich microfilm of crustaceans and worms, and prevented the flat from ever really drying out. Spotted about were boulders of dead coral, too large for the waves to wash ashore. Low tides left shallow puddles here, and at high tide the Limwei (*Charcharhinus melanopterus*), a harmless little sand shark with black-tipped fins, cruised inquisitively over the flats, often coming up to nose about my feet as I waded out to take the morning ocean temperatures.

At the shoreline itself conditions varied. In some places the reef flat gave way directly to a sandy beach. In other spots a beach-rock conglomerate of cemented rocks and shells led to a steeply sloping strand of rocks and pebbles.

Within the chosen strip of reef nearest our home we did the sorts of things that biologists do to get acquainted with a new field area. We mapped the bottom roughly along our base line. We collected and preserved samples of the plants and animals, tabulated the distribution of the commoner species, and tried to find out what they were eating. We photographed typical associations of organisms, and tried to measure such things as variations in the temperature and salinity of the marine environment under differing conditions of weather and tides. The salinity of the tidepools, we found, sometimes dropped to as low as one-sixth that of normal seawater during pouring rains at low tide. Under these conditions the body salts of marine forms tend to diffuse out through the skin and fresh water enters the body by osmosis. The results could be a disastrous salt loss, an upset in the body salt balance, and an internal rupturing of cells and tissues. Forms living on the inner reef flat have to be able either to meet this problem when it comes, or to run away from it. We expected to find very salty pools formed by evaporation at low tide, but we never did. Such evaporation as takes place in the humid air tends to be offset by a leakage of fresh water, trickling out of the beach at ebb tide from the edges of the underground lens.

Water temperature varied, too. During low tides on summer days the puddles on the reef flat sometimes got up to 40°C, giving their inhabitants a Japanese bath. Under these conditions the brittle stars would hide in crevices, protrude two or three waving arms, and undulate these faster and faster as the temperature went up. Tidepool fishes, hermit crabs, and sea cucumbers seemed unaffected.

Not all the cucumbers even stayed in pools at low tide. One tough-bodied species nearly a foot long (*Holothuria atra*) often spent the whole of a low tide period exposed to air and sun on the inner reef flat. Judging from the effects of such exposure on ourselves the beasts should have been broiled crisp, but they weren't. Marston and I had decided to have a look into the matter one blazing morning.

To begin with, the animals were jet black in color, but they habitually coated their bodies with an adhering layer of sand; so covered, they blended inconspicuously with the reef flat. Was this sandy coating a protective disguise against predaceous enemies, we wondered, or was it a protection from the sun? A black animal might be expected to absorb a lot more radiant energy than a pale form or a sand-coated one. We collected a pile of the creatures and carefully denuded half of them of sand. Some of the naked and some of the sandy animals we placed in a shallow pool; some of each batch were placed out on the drying flat nearby. We took rectal temperatures of all the animals, and temperatures of the air and pool as well, and went off to work on other things. Two hours later we came back and took all the temperatures again.

The animals that had been submerged proved much alike; all had warmed up with the water of the pool, and the naked forms ran scarcely half a degree warmer than their sandy counterparts. Out on the reef flat the difference was more conspicuous. Here, the black, denuded animals averaged 2°C higher inside than the sandy ones, and their exposed skins had a desiccated look. Somewhat unexpectedly, both groups out of water were cooler than the animals in the pool, doubtless from the effects of evaporation. It looked, then, as though the sandy coating of the body cut heat absorption, aided in evaporation, and prevented drying of the skin in animals exposed at low tide; perhaps it served as a disguise from enemies as well. And an animal that felt too hot in a pool could always crawl out onto the sun-baked reef flat to cool off.

The inner reef flats on the leeward edge of the atoll were interestingly different from those along the windward rim. Here on the western side were no islets but instead a great plain extending inward for hundreds of yards. It was never quite uncovered by the lowest tides, and in place of a smooth field the plain was dotted with a multitude of small rocks and hummocks of coral, *Millepora,* and corallines. Here, in holes and under rocks, were sea urchins, some harmless, others equipped with needle-pointed poisonous spines. We saw occasional individuals of the orange starfish *Acanthaster planci,* considered a murderous menace to bare feet by the Ifalukians because of its covering of inch-long pointed spikes coated with a toxic slime.

Almost imperceptibly things changed as one paced inward across the western reef flat. A hundred yards from the lagoon the water began to deepen gradually. More sand covered the bottom here, and the colonies of the coral *Porites* were larger and less flattened. At last heads of the blue coral *Heliopora* commenced to show up. These increased in size and number as one continued inward, now wading in waist-deep water, now swimming, and at last, at the lagoon margin of the reef, they dominated everything.

It was a region of unsurpassed loveliness here among the blue coral, a world of azure castles in a liquid crystal sea. Always I saw it with a sense of wonder that was heightened, not lessened, by a technical appreciation of the scene. On all of Ifaluk, no place was closer to fairyland.

Quite different from the circular reef of the atoll were the patch reefs in the enclosed lagoon. Here, dotting the sandy bottom, were scattered coral knolls and platforms, ranging from a few square yards to a quarter acre in extent. These little reefs abounded on the sandy lagoon shelf along the inner coast of Falarik. They were formed largely of a branched coral (*Porites andrewsi*), and they bristled with projecting fingers of pastel green and brown. In the region of our swimming hole we came to know them intimately, and here, in my more anthropomorphic moments, the reefs recalled a rabble army, deployed in a tattered line. Here a squat old warrior crouched in the shallows; there a lush camp follower rested her pleasantly rounded form in stiller, deeper waters. Out on the lagoon slope and bottom ranged the scouts in open, sparse formation.

Marston and I had been concerned with the corals and with the grosser features of these reefs; their size, form, distribution, and externally visible inhabitants. Now Ted Bayer came along with the question, "What's *inside* the patch reefs?" We went to find out, armed with geology picks, crowbars, and something of the anticipation of small boys eyeing the family alarm clock.

The coral branches broke easily, and it was soon apparent that the zone of living coral extended inward for only a few inches. Beyond this the coral was dead, its limbs and twigs encrusted with coralline algae and a fine fuzz of softer seaweeds that grew well in the shade. Still deeper in the reef these disappeared, and the old branches of the reef tangled and interlaced like the roots of a giant tree, turned to stone. Between these stretched a dark labyrinth of tunnels, crevices, and hidden chambers, and here the animals took over. The lavender and black bodies of soft tunicates coated the branches; vermillion sponges clustered like grapes; and slender shrimps in armor striped with red and green flipped themselves backwards in corridors no longer secret.

We ripped their universe apart with earthquake blows. Cracked open, the ancient coral branches showed us boring clams, the tubular burrows of peanut worms, and galleries eaten out by the acids of the yellow boring sponge. Deeper we probed the reef, and life grew steadily more sparse. Two feet in from the surface the reef was nearly solid, its passageways choked with the calcereous debris of centuries.

These general findings were not unexpected. A reef—any reef—is mostly dead material. Even a living coral is largely an inert, stony mass overlaid by a film of living tissue. Making up the film are the bodies of a myriad tiny polyps, each with its own mouth and tentacles, and each joined inseparably with its neighbors to form a colony, stretched in a living layer over the hard skeleton below. A coral grows by depositing lime in successive layers on this skeleton, and as the surface area of the colony increases, new polyps arise beside the older ones. The coral polyps are carnivorous, feeding on minute animals which they snare from the plankton with stinging tentacles or with a thin blanket of sticky mucus on the outer tissues.

Most of the reef-building corals require sunlight for normal growth. The light is not needed by the coral polyps themselves, but by a host of microscopic one-celled algae (dinoflagellates called zooxanthellae) which live within their tissues and which give to the corals their colors of green and yellow and brown. This intimate relationship of plant and animal is one of mutual advantage. The algae gain protection and a good food supply, for the discarded wastes of the coral are food and fertilizer for them. In exchange, by absorbing these wastes, the algae serve as excretory organs for the coral; too, they yield oxygen in daylight hours, and perhaps they release or leak some substance of nutritive value to the coral. They do not serve as food directly, for the coral never digests its algal boarders, even when starved of other food. If kept in the dark, the algae die and the coral extrudes them; thus deprived of its plant cells the coral can live, at least for a time, provided it gets the proper animal food, but it does not flourish normally. And so, in a reef environment, wherever the light becomes too dim for plants to grow, the reef-building corals, too, dwindle and grow scarce.

Considerations of this and other matters turned our attention to the reefs in deeper waters. What, for example, lay beyond the seaward margin with its algal ridge, beyond the rim of the atoll where the great reef sloped down toward the bottom of the sea? Work here required exceptionally calm weather, and there was always the danger of sharks. Our trips outside the ridge were few, but, together with the aerial photographs and interrogations of Ifalukian fishermen, they gave us a fair inkling of what lay beyond and below the breakers.

Out and down from the algal ridge curved the reef front, descending into the sea. The slope was gradual at first. Down the reef front ran the surge channels, widening and deepening into great gullies; between them the reef descended in sloping spurs and ridges. It was as though the front of the reef had been scratched by the teeth of a gigantic comb.

We wondered at the cause of this curious arrangement of spurs and grooves in the reef front. Studies at Bikini had shown that the buttresses and gullies made a fine breakwater, and were best developed on the windward reefs. This was true of Ifaluk, too, and here, along the windward side, where islets formed a nearly continuous barrier along the reef, the channels served as great gutters draining the reef flat. Clouds of rotenone, spread on the reef flat, moved down the bottoms of the gullies below the waves, and only rose to the surface again some distance outside the breakers. Perhaps this continuous drainage from the flat, with its sediments, tended to inhibit coral growth in these reef front grooves.

Moving outward, at first coral growth increased with depth below the surface. In some regions a few fathoms down the reef was terraced in a coral garden, in others the slope seemed more or less unbroken. Down below the ten fathom line, corals and algae began to dwindle with decreasing light. Bob Rofen was the only westerner who ever got close to that depth of Ifaluk; for the rest of us viewing things through a glass-bottomed box from the surface was never very satisfactory.

The southwest exposure of the atoll was curiously different. There, between Elangalap and Ella islets, the reef front appeared to drop down in a steep cliff. Our aerial photographs showed this clearly, and Yani verified the fact. This was the region where the great Taiyau lurked. We made an attempt to explore the area during the late summer, and the trip left a lasting impression.

Crossing the lagoon we anchored the BWUP and headed for the algal ridge. It was quite a surprise at first when we couldn't find it. We stood at the place where it surely ought to be and looked around.

There was no real ridge at all, only a smooth bench of rock in waist-deep water. Covering the bottom was a hard pavement of *Millepora* and corallines, with here and there a stubby-fingered colony of coral. At intervals the floor was raised in three-foot polished columns, some bearing a few pink heads of corallines, others topped with flat green blades of *Millepora*.

I took a small collecting sack and knife, put on my goggles, and swam slowly along the bottom, surfacing periodically for air. Sunlight and ripples cast a dancing mosaic of light on the reef. The floor of the world curved out and down, into the regions of deeper blue. A dozen yards out the bottom showed the first shallow grooves of the surge channels, and I followed one of these out.

It deepened rapidly, and soon I was in a gully six feet deep and as many across. Sparse clusters of green *Halimeda* hung from the walls, waving in the slight currents. In places the channel deepened into potholes filled with great rounded boulders, rolled smooth by the surging waters of uncounted years. The channel widened as it continued down. At a depth of twenty feet a small bed of the swaying pink seaweed *Liagora* appeared on a rock in the channel, and at twenty-five feet this was everywhere, scattered on the channel walls. Coral heads protruded here and there, but they were widely spaced; at this depth I had expected a whole forest of them.

The gully I had been following suddenly widened and came to an end. With a six-foot drop it disgorged into a pocket thirty feet across, filled with great water-smoothed boulders. I swam over it, a few feet above the rocks. Beyond was a slight rise, a lip, and then—nothing.

Nothing for the land-lubber, that is. There was a great sea cliff, and water that went from blue to black. I surfaced. The others were all a long, long way back, working on the reef flat. There was a gentle outward current, tending to carry one out beyond the last visible bottom. I began to feel rather small, naked, and defenseless. It seemed to me that man, coming from a world of solid ground, was accustomed to meeting danger coming from above and from the sides, but definitely not coming from below. Out here I felt much more at ease near the bottom than at the surface. I went down and began to move back, swimming slowly above the rocks. Gradually the distorted landscape sloped upward toward my own world of light and air. I filled the collecting bag on the trip back.

Our last encounter with the reef front came late in the fall. We took the WAT and anchored in six fathoms a few hundred yards outside Elangalap islet. In this region the reef flat and ridge were narrow, and the reef front dropped steeply for some thirty feet, then spread outward in a sloping terrace. Great chasms cut the reef front, and between them the ridges rose in giant buttresses. The whole submarine landscape was forested with the lushest growth of coral I had ever seen; the blues and greens of *Heliopora* and *Millepora*, mountainous masses of *Porites*, and a hoard of branched and antlered species of yellow and brown, some of the heads six feet or more across.

We had scarcely anchored when two of Bob's helpers discovered they had forgotten to bring their goggles. Ted Bayer and I loaned ours, for the bottom here was a bit beyond our effective diving range. We rigged a galvanized washtub on the sounding line and lowered it, preparing to look over any materials the divers collected down below. Bob put on the aqualung and spread a batch of rotenone.

Collecting conditions left something to be desired, and before long

Ted and I were satisfied we had no excuse for diving. Two good-sized sharks, apparently attracted by the pounding of geology picks, came round to investigate with more than idle curiosity. Out here there were no handy reefs to jump on. We hung shark repellent bags over the side, but the currents carried the dye away rapidly, along with the cloud of rotenone. Several times we splashed like mad and banged things to create a diversion, and twice everyone piled into the WAT in a mad rush. Still, the collection was a rich one, a tempting indication that there was much more down below for some future party to exploit. Bob got a number of rare fishes that were taken nowhere else, and it took Ted Bayer two days to annotate and preserve the collection of invertebrates.

With all of our work in the Ifaluk marine realm, our picture of the atoll reef was crude and fragmentary; the longer we looked the more apparent this became. The reef was a thing of magnificent size and awesome complexity, and we looked at it with different eyes; each of us saw the things for which he had been trained to look, and perhaps a bit more, and each formed an impression framed by a point of view that was less than panoramic.

To a geologist an atoll reef is a great mass of limestone, formed from the loose and consolidated skeletons of coral and other forms of life. It represents a sort of mountainous boneyard accumulated slowly over the millennia. The geologist looks at the size of the pile, its thickness, its general shape and detailed form, and its composition at various levels. To his eyes these things yield clues to the age of the reef, to the actions of wind and wave now and in the past; they hint at prehistoric shifts in the level of the sea and of its bottom, and even tell of temperature changes in ancient times. Limestone the reef may be, but in the historical perspective of the geologist's mind it is no rock of ages but a changing, dynamic thing. The geologist, of course, is conscious of the life on the reef, but he is not really professionally concerned with most things that can still move under their own power.

The marine biologist sees the reef in a rather different way; indeed, in about as many different ways as there are marine biologists. To him the reef is a rich community of living things, dominated in places by corals and their relatives or by the stony coralline algae, but harboring

many other forms. Like the geologist, he is interested in the growth
and form of reefs, but his main concern is with the soft parts, not the
hard ones. He sees, spread over the limestone mountain, like the frost-
ing on a cake, a thin and often beautiful layer of life. Taxonomically
it is appallingly complex, for nearly every major group of organisms
is represented here, some by many species.

The biologist sees the diversity of habit and habitat upon the reef;
at every level there are crawlers and swimmers on the surface, attached
animals and plants, burrowers in the stone, nestlers in crevices and
weed, and planktonic drifters in the sea above. He thinks of organisms
in terms of their food relations to one another, too; the plants producing organic matter, in places as productively as in a cornfield;
the animals consuming the plants and one another; and the micro-
organisms synthesizing, reducing, and transforming substances, balanc-
ing the biological books. Within this community, each separate individual seeks matter and energy in forms that it can use, protects itself from entities and forces that would destroy it, and multiplies itself
in endless cycles, each species using a combination of ways, places,
and things specific for its kind alone. Yet the activities of each are
somehow linked to those of all the others, and within this tangled
network of relationships a dynamic and uneasy balance is maintained
—the so-called "balance of nature" on the reef.

The biologist, swamped by this complexity, tends to ignore the
mountain of lime beneath his feet, and is inclined to leave the di-
mension of history to the geologist, if one is available. The geologist,
on the other hand, tends to emphasize the moulding of gross form by
environmental forces, past and present, and is less concerned with
who eats whom, except for forms with a taste for geologists. Taken
together, the views give a broader perspective.

It needs this sort of perspective to deal with such a question as,
"How is an atoll formed?" It was a query young Charles Darwin had
put to himself on his famous voyage on the BEAGLE. Atolls with
lagoons had been discovered in the Indian Ocean and in many parts
of the Pacific. It was well known that reefs thrived only in the shallows, and most people who worried about such things considered
that atolls were merely reefs growing on the rims of submerged
volcanic craters.

Darwin's own experience with reefs was not extensive. He had seen atolls from the ship, passing through the Tuamotus, but the BEAGLE had not stopped there. At Tahiti he spent most of his time in the green mountains and valleys, but he had seen the reefs, too; the fringing reefs, separated from the shore by a narrow strip of shallows a few feet deep, and the larger barrier reefs, lying a mile or two offshore and separated from the main islands by deep lagoons. One Sunday, after paddling about the reefs in a canoe, he noted in his diary, "It is my opinion, that . . . little is yet known, in spite of the much which has been written, of the structure & origin of the Coral Islands & reefs." *

Half a year later the BEAGLE put in for eleven days at the Cocos-Keeling Islands, a pair of atolls in the Indian Ocean. It was Darwin's first (and last) chance to explore lagoon islands at first hand. He visited the reefs, studied the lagoon, and accompanied the ship as it made offshore soundings. And as the BEAGLE sailed away, he wrote in his diary, April 12th, 1836:

"In the morning we stood out of the Lagoon. I am glad we have visited these Islands; such formations surely rank high amongst the wonderful objects of this world. It is not a wonder which at first strikes the eye of the body, but rather after reflection, the eye of reason. We feel surprised when travellers relate accounts of the vast piles & extent of some ancient ruins; but how insignificant are the greatest of these, when compared to the matter here accumulated by various small animals. Throughout the whole group of Islands, every single atom, even from the most minute particle to large fragments of rocks, bear the stamp of once having been subjected to the power of organic arrangement. Capt. FitzRoy at the distance of but little more than a mile from the shore sounded with a line 7200 feet long, & found no bottom. Hence we must consider this Isd as the summit of a lofty mountain; to how great a depth or thickness the work of the Coral animal extends is quite uncertain. If the opinion that the rock-making Polypi continue to build upwards as the foundation of the Isd from volcanic agency, after intervals, gradually subsides, is granted to be true; then probably the Coral limestone must be of great thickness.

* Barlow, Nora (editor), *Charles Darwin's Diary of the Voyage of H.M.S. Beagle,* Cambridge University Press, 1934.

We see certain Isds in the Pacifick, such as Tahiti & Eimeo . . . which are encircled by a Coral reef separated from the shore by channels & basins of still water. Various causes tend to check the growth of the most efficient kinds of Corals in these situations. Hence if we imagine such an Island, after long successive intervals to subside a few feet . . . the coral would be continued upwards, rising from the foundation of the encircling reef. In time the central land would sink beneath the level of the sea & disappear, but the coral would have completed its circular wall. Should we not then have a Lagoon Island?—Under this view, we must look at a Lagoon Isd as a monument raised by myriads of tiny architects, to mark the spot where a former land lies buried in the depths of the ocean." *

Longer accounts developing this thesis appeared in a paper a year later, in his famous Journal of Researches, and in his volume on Coral Reefs, but the essence of the concept is here, in a rough manuscript never intended to see print. In some parts of the world the land was elevating; it followed that in others it must be subsiding, "otherwise," as he put it later, "the whole globe would have swollen." Reefs started as fringing reefs about tropic islands of volcanic origin. If the land was stable or elevating slowly, they remained as fringing reefs, growing or eroding to the point where they were just awash at the lowest tides. But if the land subsided at a rate that could be matched by the upward growth of corals, the reef would continue to reach for the surface, gradually transforming into a barrier reef and finally a ring-shaped atoll.

Darwin's theory found its supporters and critics. Many modifications and alternative concepts have since been proposed, and even today there is much disagreement and a general feeling that no one theory covers all atolls. Darwin himself, in 1881, the year before his death, wrote to the wealthy zoologist Alexander Agassiz, saying: "I wish that some doubly rich millionaire would take it into his head to have borings made in some of the Pacific and Indian Atolls, and bring home cores for slicing from a depth of 500 to 600 feet."

He never lived to see it. The deep drilling of reefs began at Funafuti

---

* Barlow, Nora (editor), *Charles Darwin's Diary of the Voyage of H.M.S. Beagle*, Cambridge University Press, 1934.

Atoll in 1897; since then several islands, and reefs near continental areas, have been deeply probed, most recently the atom-bombed atolls of Bikini and Eniwetok, over a thousand miles to the east of Ifaluk. At Bikini the rock bit was still working in reef detritus at 2556 feet; on Eniwetok the drill finally hit hard volcanic rock 4154 feet down. Oddly enough, the great bulk of old reef material at levels below the surface is relatively loose and unconsolidated, and through this porous mass the sea can slowly percolate.

Evidence from the deep borings, from seismic refractions, and from elevated reefs 1000 feet thick on islands here and there, all indicates that subsidence of the sea floor has been an important factor in atoll formation. Some reefs may have started on submarine sea mounts (guyots) with peaks reaching into the lighted zone where corals grow. Sea mounts, though, tend to have smooth and slightly rounded tops, beveled by the sea; seismic echoes from atolls in the Marshall group show less regular rock surfaces beneath the ancient reef, suggesting the mountains may have protruded as islands when the reefs first formed upon them.

Even with subsidence and reef upgrowth well-established in several areas, the situation is not so simple as Darwin saw it; for, as his successors have shown, the sea surface has fluctuated in level as well as the sea bottom. During the ice ages the ocean level dropped, a part of its waters locked in the mountainous glaciers that crept over a sixth of the world's land. As the sea receded, the upper regions of the reefs became exposed and died. Weathering by wind, rain, and sea must have cut down many a reef and planed it off at the new level of the sea. Cooling of the oceans possibly killed the reefs entirely in marginal areas, but in others coral growth probably continued uninterrupted below the surface of the sea. With slow melting of glaciers and further subsidence of the bottom, "new" reefs grew upward on the bases of the old, at rates of perhaps one to four millimeters a year. The cores taken at Bikini indicate the reef was exposed and resubmerged several times, though it isn't clear how much was due to elevation and subsidence of the sea floor and how much to changes in sea level.

Reconstructing the past history of a coral island always involves some speculation, but geologists do the best they can with incomplete evidence. On Ifaluk Josh thought the ten fathom depth of the submarine terraces beyond the reef front and of parts of the lagoon bottom suggested that a former sea stand, perhaps in a late glacial period, had truncated the once higher atoll at this level. Subsequently the sea had risen and the atoll reef had grown upward with it, perhaps to near its present height. The 5½ fathom depths of the limestone formations around the lagoon bank and in the ship pass might reflect, he thought, a later lesser drop in sea level, again followed by rising waters and reef upgrowth.

This later rise very likely brought the atoll to an elevation somewhat above the present level of the sea and reef. Josh noted remnants of consolidated rubble some two and a half feet above the present high tide level on Falalap, and an elevated ridge—probably a reef remnant—on the reef flat east of southern Falarik. These things, he felt, indicated a sea stand perhaps a meter above its present level, not more than a few thousands of years ago. Many other Pacific atolls show somewhat similar exposed ledges and pinnacles of hard reef rock above the present sea level. They indicate that the sea has not yet risen to its former height since the last glacial period. We are at the tail end of an ice age, for the glaciers are still melting, raising the level of the world's seas by about 0.6 millimeters a year.

Looked at in one way, then, the atolls of today are relatively recent structures, dating only from the last glacial period; from another standpoint they are much more venerable, the present reefs and islets being based, in turn, on a series of older reefs.

It isn't completely clear from all of this why so many atolls should retain central lagoons. We know, as did Darwin and his predecessors, that reefs flourish best near their outer margins. In the case of a circular reef, this produces a cup-shaped structure. The sediments carried over the rim and deposited in the center inhibit most coral growth here. But exposure and weathering during glacial periods cut down the reefs, and the accumulation of sediments tends to fill the lagoons. We might therefore expect to find many atolls with their lagoons all filled up—coral islands resembling plates rather than rings. Such atolls are uncommon.

Actually, lagoons do appear to be filling up, but it is apparently a slow process. The smaller atolls, like Ifaluk, which have a greater circumference in proportion to the area of the lagoon, appear to be filling more rapidly than the larger atolls—at least the smaller atolls have shallower lagoons. Still, it has puzzled geologists that over much of the Pacific, the larger atolls have lagoons of pretty much the same depth, thirty–forty-five fathoms. Possibly this represents a base level below which the action of waves cannot stir the sediments to be carried off. More likely, the level reflects the effects of a lowering of the oceans during a great period of glacial advance. As in so many fields of work, there are more problems than answers, and most scientists like it that way.

CHAPTER XVI

WOLEAI AND TILIMWOL

I DOZED on my cot, listening with half an ear to the vague noises of Ifaluk waking up and going about its early morning chores. Dawn had come but there was still a twilight dimness about things. A Micronesian starling gave a raucous call, and a rooster answered from somewhere up by Falepenach canoe house. Through half-closed eyes I saw a pair of brown legs, tattooed with rows of blue porpoises, walking close to the Fan Nap. They stopped opposite the head of my bed. In a moment Yani was squatting and ducking his head under the thatched eaves.

He peered sharply for a moment, unable to see through the mosquito net in the dimness.

"Don?" He whispered so as not to wake the others. "Don?"

I said, "Hi, brother. What's up?" in my best Ifalukian, which only Yani really understood.

He had news. Four canoes had been sighted, sailing in from the west. They were still on the horizon, far outside Elangalap, and would not be in for quite a while. They were probably from Woleai, he said; nothing else lay nearby in that direction.

The WAT had taken off with Tom and Bob's regular crew of helpers some time ago, as soon as the canoes had been sighted. They had the outboard and were already outside Elangalap, which meant that if we wanted to go anywhere we would have to row the BWUP. I put on shorts, took the binoculars, and went down to the lagoon beach with Yani.

The canoes were still specks in the distance, and it was a wonder they had been spotted at all in the early dawn. The Ifalukian eye has an uncanny ability to pick up small points on the horizon. Probably someone had seen the canoes from the top of a coconut tree. I left Yani with the binoculars and went off to take the daily weather data and the ocean and lagoon temperatures. Bob and Ted were up when I got back.

There was no need for discussion. Working day or not, we all wanted to go out to meet the visitors. Skipping breakfast we shoved off in the BWUP with Yani and Tom's brother Magaleisei. With two at the oars and the rest paddling, we were soon through the ship pass and outside the atoll, beyond the south coast of Ella islet.

Here we stopped. Except for a slight swell the sea was as calm as the lagoon. Several Ifaluk canoes were here already. Old Gauaisig nodded his balding head at us and paddled slowly by. A small boy sat back to back with him in the narrow canoe, bailing diligently.

The voyagers were still half a mile off, approaching slowly in single file. In the morning sun their pandanus sails formed golden triangles against the clouds. Here in the open sea the black canoes seemed small and frail for a blue-water voyage. The WAT rounded the tip of Ella islet, coming from Elangalap.

A few hundred yards from us the two leading canoes hove to. The sails came down, were quickly furled about the unstepped masts and laid aside. Paddles were dipped to hold the boats at rest. The narrow hulls rocked gently in the swell, spreading outriggers balanced by the high platforms projecting on the opposite side.

The third canoe sailed in and joined them. Yani touched my arm and nodded toward a dark figure riding on its platform. It was, he said, the highest ranking chief of Woleai. We eased the BWUP in that direction, and when the chief saw us coming he quickly removed a wreath of flowers from his head and clapped on a rather ancient tropical helmet. He sat on his platform as on a throne, a heavy-set man in his middle fifties, with short gray hair and a moderate paunch. He allowed us to take some pictures, and graciously presented the BWUP with five cigarettes and some drinking coconuts. We thanked him; the coconuts were a step toward breakfast, and it was a pleasant change to be receiving cigarettes instead of passing them around.

The last canoe came up and stashed its sails. Flanked by an Ifalukian escort, the four vessels paddled toward the ship pass. The WAT
puttered alongside the BWUP and magnanimously offered to tow us
home. Bob transferred to the rubber boat, and the motor actually ran
most of the way back to Rauau village before giving up. We rowed in,
leaving the WAT behind with its fuming mechanics.

As befitted custom, the chiefs of Ifaluk had seated themselves with
dignity on the lawn just in front of the Fan Nap. Maroligar invited us
to join them. The Woleai canoes moved in and beached in front of us,
and official greetings were not exchanged until the visiting chiefs had
placed themselves comfortably beside those of Ifaluk. We were introduced around in turn. I understood very little of the conversation that
followed; after a polite interval we excused ourselves and finished
breakfast.

The big canoes had now been pulled up on the beach and unloaded. The ordinary people of Ifaluk crowded around, bringing coconuts and food and talking with the visitors. The canoe captains saw
to the safe arrangement of their vessels, tied small squares of cloth
over the jutting prongs at either end of the canoes, and came to sit in
a group on the grass a little distance from their chiefs. The rest of the
visitors and a body of local men gathered on the grass in the background.

Maroligar asked us to join the chiefly circle again. It was clear that
we were a prime attraction to the visitors, that our island was proud
of us, and that Ifaluk's chiefs wanted to exhibit us to good advantage.
So we sat decoratively in a conspicuous spot and tried hard to appear a credit to the atoll that claimed us. After a time we made a gift
to the visitors, a box of twist tobacco for each canoe. It was received
with the obvious pleasure of confirmed smokers viewing the end of a
tobacco famine, and the leading chief accepted the present with a
short speech of thanks. Then Maroligar asked us to take pictures of
the dignitaries, and we obliged. Bob's Polaroid camera, which delivered finished prints on the spot, made an instant hit, and it struck us
that this should be standard equipment for expeditions to far off spots.
Bob took many pictures and gave them all away, and in no time the
morning had drifted pleasantly by.

I gathered from Tom and Yani that the trip was a social affair, a visit to exchange greetings and gossip. Woleai had doubtless heard of our presence from travelling islanders on the METOMKIN, and wanted a look at us, but an excuse like that was not really needed. Ordinarily the visiting chiefs would have bunked in the Fan Nap, but with us there they were fixed up comfortably in Rolong canoe house, just next door. Most of the other travellers stayed in the households of relatives on Ifaluk, for the family groupings on the two islands are essentially the same. The similarity, according to local history, dated back to the repopulation of Woleai atoll from Ifaluk after Maur's bloody conquest, somewhere in the misty past.

The Woleai visit lasted three days. We managed to get our scheduled work done, in spite of interesting interruptions like the one which came late the following afternoon. I was flat on my belly in the turtle grass beds, collecting the flora and fauna, when the first of the Ifaluk love songs sounded out in the still air.

Women singing—a whole group of them; this was something unusual. Immediately I beached my equipment and went by the Fan Nap to pick up a camera. Maroligar was there, and he waved an arm toward Falepenach canoe house. Even as I got there a procession of women arrived, dressed in bright new skirts, wreaths, and bits of red cloth. Bob and Ted were on the sidelines already.

Near the open front of the canoe house sat the chiefs of Woleai, and near them the canoe captains. Not another man was in sight. Draped to the ears in floral wreaths, the visitors were the center of attention of two groups of local women. Out in front stood the cream of Ifaluk's Junior League, in a triple line. Yani's wife Letaweriur was there with some twenty other beauties. And to the side stood a line of older women, led by Bakal's mother Tawerimis. The newcomers joined the women already in place, and all of them sang and danced for the Woleai chiefs.

It was an affair of high spirits and informality, of gay laughter, hand clapping, shouts, and the stamping of bare feet. And from time to time the ladies paraded up to the chiefs to load them with more garlands.

The men of Ifaluk were not supposed to hear their own women

singing love songs in public, but it was a safe bet that some careful auditing was going on from a respectable distance. Yani was up in a coconut tree, collecting hachi, and he heard most of the songs. He explained some of them the next day. Some were love songs in the sentimental tradition, sung for a man away from home ("I miss you very much; come home to me and I will make wreaths for you"). One was the song of a lady pointing out her attractions to a man ("See, I am not a fat woman; look, you can count my ribs"). This sounded like pure fun, and provoked a lot of giggles, for the group that danced it included some of the fattest women on the atoll. Finally, there were a few of the personal songs that a woman sings to her husband or lover when they are alone together. It was a good show. If the earlier dances we had seen had been ritual and classic, this was vaudeville; the Woleai chiefs enjoyed it, and so did we.

Two days later the canoes sailed home. Tewas came by at dawn to tell us he had decided to go with them, and that he wanted his last week's pay in tobacco, to stave off the shortage on Woleai. I counted out a money equivalent in twists and cigarettes. When the canoes were nearly ready, we went down to see them off. The great hulls rested gently in the water on the lagoon shelf. Loading was still going on, and people waded to and from the shore with bundles of husked drinking coconuts and other gifts.

We said good-bye to the chiefs, and the passengers climbed aboard. Five people from Ifaluk, among them Tewas and an attractive girl, had received permission from the Ifaluk chiefs to go along. They waded out and climbed in. Yani, standing beside me, indicated the girl.

"Very funny story about that lady. Sometime I tell you." He was trying to keep a straight face.

I said, "Tell me now, brother—maybe later you forget," but, satisfied at having roused my curiosity, he only laughed and changed the subject.

Paddles appeared, and the big black and red canoes glided past the shadowy patch reefs and moved southward over the lagoon. Near the southern pass the masts were raised and the sails set. A light breeze caught them, and they were on the way. We watched them until they

ABOVE The ocean side of Ella was strewn with coral boulders.

LEFT There was a small, brackish pond near the western end of Ella, screened by *Pemphis trees*. PHOTO BY BAYER

BELOW The lagoon shore of Ella looked like a proper tropical beach.

LEFT Five hundred pounds of "tilimwol" were dipped out of the lagoon in a few hours during a run.

ABOVE The women of Ifaluk put on a song and dance for the visitors from Woleai.

BELOW The captains of the visiting Woleai canoes. PHOTO BY BAYER

disappeared behind Ella islet. How much longer, I wondered, would a world that talked of rocket ships see such a sight; canoes of hand-adzed beams, lashed together with hand-rolled rope, catching the wind with sails of woven mats, and guided by men whose compass was the sky?

On the other hand, this culture might outlast our own.

Tom joined us, remarking conversationally, "Dat canoe, 'e got good wind." We walked down the beach a bit. People were dispersing, but a small group around Maroligar was already at work, lashing sticks and poles into a strong framework some ten feet long and three feet wide. At first glance it looked like the skeleton for a midget Quonset hut or a large bathtub.

Tom waved a hand at it. " 'E catch dat small fish 'longside dat lagoon," he said. By the end of the day the frame was finished, and we saw with some surprise that it had been lined with copper screen from an ancient greenish roll that lay on the beach nearby. It looked like a fish trap, but it had no door and no covering over the open bottom.

We woke next morning to the sound of distant shouts, coming from the lagoon. In a minute we were up and on the beach. Four medium-sized canoes formed an open square out on the lagoon shelf, and the din arose from men in the boats and in the water nearby. Two of the wire-lined contraptions were in operation, and we saw at once that these were really giant basket sieves. Handled by teams of several men, they were lowered into the water, scooped forward, lifted, and dumped into the canoe, in repeated movements. The men in the water seemed to be doing most of the work, but each scoop was guided by poles attached at either end, handled by men in the canoes. And as the scoops moved up and down, other men in the water pushed the boats slowly along the shelf.

We ate and did the morning routine, and by that time the canoes were in. The catch was dumped on coconut leaf mats near the beach, a large pile of a handsome blue and silver fish about the size of small sardines. Toroman held one up and said, "Tilimwol."

Bob gave a startled exclamation; with all his collecting he had never seen the fish before, and offhand he wasn't even sure of the family of fishes to which it belonged. He hurried back to the Fan Nap for a look at his fish books. It turned out to be something called *Pterocaesio tile;* I liked the name Tilimwol better. I went to get the scales and the notebook we used for recording communal fish catches. By the time I got back, Yani, who had been out with the other men, was dried off and ready to join me in estimating the catch.

Toroman did the dividing, as usual. As a unit of measure he used all the fish that could be scooped up between his open hand and a half coconut shell. We weighed a sample series of his scoops and they averaged around four pounds, with ninety–ninety-five fishes to a pound. The distribution began, Toroman calling out the name of each household in turn: "Welipi! Soumat! Faraik! Falepenach! Falolorik! Nuteitei!" And so on, down the line. As the name was called, a man from the household brought up a coconut leaf basket and received a number of scoops appropriate to the size of his family. Yani and I counted the number of scoops given to each family, and weighed the shares of Falepenach and Falolorik, where we were still keeping food records.

Adding things up afterward, the catch for Rauau and Falarik villages amounted to about 380 pounds, representing some 35,000 fish. Falalap's quarter-share of the catch had been assigned before unloading the canoes, Toroman said. Years of dividing catches had given him a pretty good eye for such things; added to the figures for Falarik islet this brought the total catch to about 500 pounds, nearly two pounds apiece for every man, woman, and child on the atoll.

Ifaluk held the Tilimwol in special regard. Our first indication came when Bob asked for a sample of the catch for his collection. He got a scoop of fish, but the chiefs asked him not to slit their bellies, as he usually did to allow the formaldehyde to penetrate. Bob agreed, and let them watch the pickling just to make sure.

Ted brought up a second observation during lunch. He had seen Maroligar carry a basket of fish over to the Fan Nap and place it below the Phallus of Maur. Putting his hands behind him and lowering his head, Maroligar had spoken quietly for a minute, then picked up the basket and carried it off. It was difficult to avoid interpreting this as a prayer of thanks, though we had not seen this done for any other catch.

A third surprise came when we started to make plans for an afternoon collecting trip. Our assistants politely declined to help, and Yani explained that for four days after the start of a Tilimwol run, no man on the island was allowed to do any other sort of work.

This looked as though it might apply to visitors, too, so we called on Tom for some further information. First, did the ban include us? Tom and Yani weren't sure, but there was a certain uncomfortableness about the discussion that suggested we had better resolve any doubts in favor of the local regulations. Next to come up was the question of "What constitutes work?"

At home such a question might have led to nearly endless hair-splitting and bickering. Ifaluk, it turned out, took the simple view that work meant such things as fishing for any other fish, climbing trees for food, and building nets and canoes. There was nothing to keep the women from cooking or working in the bwol, or the men from sitting around in groups and talking. And most of our own regular activities, aside from expeditions to collect fishes and edible invertebrates, were not considered work at all.

It seemed to me just as well that the Pacific Science Board wasn't around to hear that. At any rate, it was a judgment in our favor for the next four days. And maybe, after all, what we were doing *wasn't* work. The next four days were occupied with such things as interrogations, canning specimens, and the taking and writing up of field notes. When we wanted to do anything that might look like work to Ifalukian eyes, we asked beforehand and got a chiefly decision.

In going over the food records and fish notes, I found the data too skimpy to allow me to list the species in the order of their importance to man as food. We needed such a list, to help us concentrate our further efforts on the most important fishes. Yani and Tachim were lounging with others on the grass outside the Fan Nap; I recognized Aueligar's horselaugh bellowing out from time to time. I joined the group and told them what I needed. Obviously it wasn't work, for it could be done very well in a horizontal position. They agreed to try to help.

There was no disagreement among the men as to the number one food fish; it was the Garangap, a tuna (*Euthynnus*). It seemed to me an odd fish to head the list, for I had seen none during our visit, but

Ted Burrows had described vividly an occasion when a big school of tuna had entered the lagoon.

Maroligar had spotted the school at dawn, and his leather-lunged shouts of "Garangap e!" had roused the island. Canoes were hauled to the water, seines unrolled and loaded into them, and every able-bodied male joined the effort to take the school. There were only four places along the lagoon shore where it was considered possible to surround the school effectively. Seines were spread in a great crescent at one of these, and canoes lined up along the net. Another fleet of canoes set out to round up the school and drive it into the seine. Women danced and swung their hips along the shore, singing love songs to encourage the men while the net was slowly drawn around the school.

A good haul of tuna could feed the island for weeks. There were no refrigerators, but the fish lasted well if continuously smoked over a hot smudge fire. Schools had been taken four times this year before our arrival, and twice the catch was so large that Ifaluk sent canoes with surplus fish to Woleai.

Everyone agreed that the next most important food fish was the Oerik, a small goatfish (*Mulloidichthys samoensis*). These pale, finger-sized creatures with whisker-like barbels trailing from their chins were common about our swimming hole. We often saw little groups of them hunting along the bottom, repeatedly taking in small mouthfulls of detritus and blowing out the inedible sand. Large numbers were taken in wicker withe traps set on the lagoon bottom near shore.

The little animals are cooked whole, in packages of leaves over a fire, and there is a special routine for eating them. One takes a fish, breaks off the head and tail, and peels off the skin. The body is then broken in half along its length, the spine and viscera removed, and the rest eaten. I have seen finicky people do almost exactly the same thing with sardines at home. A local story has it that if eaten without the proper ritual and respect, the Oerik will leave the atoll en masse. Yani had his private doubts about this; he knew Josh had unwittingly eaten one whole some weeks before, and the fish were still abundant.

It got harder and harder to list fishes in any very reliable order of importance as we went on. High on the list were the Hali, an olive-brown sea bass with blue spots (*Epinephelus hexagonatus*), the Mol, a big-eyed, red-striped squirrel fish (*Myripristis murdjan*), several parrotfishes (*Scarus*), and a rudder fish (*Kyphosus vaigiensis*) which Ifaluk called the Rel.

The Rel was a handsome fish, a plump, silver-sided creature with big staring eyes, common about the lagoon patch reefs. Marston and I had watched this fish from the start, and it was difficult not to, for the interest was clearly mutual. Whenever we entered the lagoon the Rel came in a school, wide-eyed and silent as ghosts. Slowly they would cruise in a circle about us, keeping at a distance of a few feet. The surveillance often went on for several minutes if we stayed reasonably still. It was only later that we discovered this behavior was related to the Rel's coprophagous habits.

How much fish did Ifaluk get in a year? Near the end of our stay I added up all the figures we had for four months—communal catches and family food records—and making some pretty shaky assumptions I came up with a minimal figure. *If* the four month figure had been typical, and *if* our family food records were a good sample, Ifaluk netted around eleven tons of fish a year.

Was our period typical? The Tilimwol run had been exceptional; the little fish came in large numbers only once in a decade. But to balance this, there had been less Rop fishing on the reef than usual, and our figures didn't include the catches of tuna and flying fish earlier in the year. On the whole, Tom and Yani thought people ate about as much fish during our stay as at most other times—perhaps a shade less.

How about the family food records? We tried to make these complete and quantitative, but some fish were doubtless cooked and eaten on the beach as soon as they were caught, and before they could be counted and weighed. We always asked about this, but it wasn't an easy thing to take into account when it happened. Probably the actual total yearly catch ran closer to fourteen or fifteen tons of fish, with considerable variation from year to year. Of this total, about two-thirds was taken in large-scale community fishing ventures, the rest by individuals and small groups.

Bob Rofen was sure that the islanders were exploiting the fishes of the lagoon and reef edges most effectively; any improvement here and they would be eating into their biological capital instead of living on the interest, gradually depleting the fishery resources. There was room for increasing the yearly catch on Ifaluk, but only through a more effective exploitation of the open sea beyond the island reefs. With the present canoes and fishing gear, it was hard to see how this could be done.

Fishing for the Tilimwol went on. The second day's catch was enormous, close to 2000 pounds, and poor Toroman was a weary man when the dividing was done. On succeeding days the totals dropped to between 100 and 300 pounds a day.

Early on the fifth day we were ready for field collecting again; there remained only the matter of replacing Bob's helper Tewas, who had gone to Woleai. I went with Yani to ask Maroligar if he would assign us another man, a strong diver who could help Bob in event of trouble with the aqualung. Maroligar agreed. He and Yani got into a long conversation, and I left to get equipment ready. When Yani returned the two of us set out for our northern reef profile. As we walked along the trail, he casually remarked that this would be the last day he could work for us, and the last day for Bakal and Tachim, as well.

I must have stopped dead in my tracks with surprise. I remember thinking "What could we have done that brought this about?"

I said, "Why, brother?"

Calm and seemingly untroubled, he explained. Maroligar had agreed to find a diver for us. In the discussion afterward he had remarked to Yani that we really ought to get a whole new set of assistants. We paid our men the standard Trust Territory wage for outer islands—a dollar a day, or its equivalent in tobacco, fishhooks, knives, or whatever else we had that was wanted and could be spared. Maroligar had told Yani it wasn't fair for a few men to benefit in this way while others got nothing. The well-diggers and the men who sold Bob their unusual fishes had profited, of course, but not to the same extent. There had been no complaints, Maroligar said, but he felt it would be only fair to give some other men a chance to work for pay.

And of course the chief was right; the present situation wasn't fair.

What hurt was the thought of losing our friends Yani, Bakal, and Tachim. They were intelligent men, capable and now well-trained in the things we needed done. Moreover, in the field they were colleagues and collaborators rather than assistants; they instructed us in some things, as we instructed them in others. We enjoyed their company as comrades, and there was the smooth working rapport of a team among us.

Each of them was unique, and they supplemented each other and ourselves. Yani was the scholar of the lot; a good fisherman and provider for his family, he was nevertheless quieter and more intro-spective than the rest. His mind inquired into the general nature of things and processes; he led the others intellectually, but he was not himself a leader. Bakal, youngest of the lot, was the man of action, a doer full of courage and restless energy. Seeing him now, I could un-derstand why he had not made a good dishwasher. Perhaps, with maturity, he would be a leader of men; Yani had said that someday Bakal might become a chief. Tachim, the oldest, was the Jack-of-all-trades, dependable, vociferous, and sentimental. With his jokes, his clowning, and his fine sense of the ridiculous, he was the oil that made the wheels turn smoothly. Never, in the time remaining, could we develop such a group and spirit again.

Appropriately, perhaps, it began to pour rain. Yani and I worked hard all morning on the reef anyway, heading home about noon.

At lunch Bob, Ted, and I had a conference. There was no question of bucking Maroligar's decision; in the first place, he was the local government, and we were his guests; in the second, he was a friend, and we agreed with his judgment in this matter. We decided we would ask the chiefs if we might keep our old assistants to help train the new men. By the time they all knew the ropes it would be time for us to pack and leave anyway.

We called in Bakal, Yani, and Tachim, and were surprised to learn that they had planned to do this all along. Maroligar had not said they could not help us; he had merely said that the men now getting paid would be replaced by others. For the first time the three men seemed a bit puzzled and upset. Tachim, rarely in a serious mood, gave an impassioned speech in Ifalukian. In essence, he said, "You have paid us for our work, but we did not work for you for pay. We have helped you because you are our friends and brothers, because we wanted to help you. If you think we would stop this work merely because you cease to pay us, you have sorely misjudged us." There were tears in his eyes, and Yani and Bakal were with him one hundred percent.

I could hardly trust my voice. I think Bob and Ted felt much the same way. We had some strong handclasps all around, and went back to work. We would seek chiefly approval of this plan tonight.

Tom was at the Fan Nap when we returned, late in the afternoon. He looked irritated and angry. He had heard about Maroligar's decision and, quite unlike our men, he questioned it.

"No business dat Ifaluk man," he said. "Dat Maroligar no (under) 'stand 'bout you work. You tell Maroligar no business dat Ifaluk chief!"

This was the last sort of reaction we wanted stirred up. I found myself taking Maroligar's side, arguing vigorously for the wisdom and justice of his decision. Of course the chief was right, and of course we would do as he said. We needed only to ask the chiefs whether our three men could continue to help us without pay, while the new men learned their jobs.

Tom looked at me. Perhaps for a moment he thought I was lying to him. He was certainly enough of a realist to see that if we insisted strongly enough on anything, the chiefs would give in to us. I am sure he was aware that I knew it too. I hoped he could understand that we were trying to arrange things so that both sides could have their cake and eat it too.

Tom was a good politician. Whatever he saw and thought, he was at ease again.

"Oh, more better dat way, I t'ink," he nodded. He agreed to ask the chiefs if we might see them that evening.

The chiefs gathered on the lawn back of the Fan Nap as we were getting supper. We shut down the stove and went out to sit with them, passing around a box of raisins. After appropriate greetings and a polite pause, I spoke slowly in English, and Tom translated. He did a straight job, and any fears I had had that he would try to defend our interests proved groundless.

Ted Burrows had written of the Ifalukian love of diplomatic "fine talk." I began by thanking the Ifaluk chiefs for their many kindnesses to all of us during our stay. I brought up Maroligar's decision, and spoke of the wisdom and justice of it; America was proud to have the islands ruled by such thoughtful leaders. We looked forward to working with the new men to be assigned to us.

The chiefs smiled and nodded, waiting politely for me to go on. I then raised the matter of keeping the old assistants, without pay, to help train the new men. Our old helpers had learned many things; they knew the fish that Bob had taken, and the ones he didn't have; they could run the motor by themselves, mix and spread the fish poison, and properly sort and preserve the fish. Above all, they knew enough English to answer our questions and to instruct us; few others did, despite my periodic evening classes.

Finally, I mentioned a possibility that the three of us had thought worth bringing up. We did not have the money and goods to hire everyone, but islanders who wanted to work for pay might come to us, find out what things we wanted, and get these for us. Within the limits of our stocks and budget, we would pay for them.

Tom finished translating the last sentence, and I indicated I was done.

The discussion that followed between the Ifaluk chiefs was a brief one. They looked to Maroligar to answer. He spoke from his position, cross-legged on the grass, his strong seamed face with short gray hair and stubble beard shining in the lamplight. Tom translated, but such was the personality of the chief that we seemed to be hearing his words directly.

In essence, Maroligar said, "The Ifaluk chiefs understand your position perfectly. Here on Ifaluk we respect the men who know their jobs and do them well. When we want to build a canoe, we get a sennap (master-builder); when we want to sail to another island, we get a palu (captain-navigator)."

It was therefore completely reasonable to him, Maroligar went on, that we should want assistants who knew their jobs. He had, he said, spent much of the day asking various young men whether they understood how to do the things our helpers did for us. And he had found no one.

In view of this, there would be no new helpers. Our present men—Yaniseman, Bakalimar, and Tachiwelimeng—were to go on working for us as usual. He would add a new man, the diver we had requested; otherwise things were to go on as before.

He was finished.

This seemed such an about-face that I explained again, that we agreed with the justice of his first decision, that we would take on and train such new helpers as he chose.

Maroligar smiled at me tolerantly and shook his head. It was as though he had said, "Young man, I appreciate your courteous efforts to save my face, but there is no need for that sort of thing here." In the absence of capable replacements, he had decided that his position was unreasonable, and that any compromise now would be unworthy of him. He seemed so at ease that we let things drift to an end.

The other chiefs beamed broadly at us now, and there was a resounding round of "Egatr mauas!" (It is excellent!) from Fagolier, Toroman, and Wolpaitik. And from ourselves. The box of raisins went around again but there were few left. Fagolier had been holding it during the talking, and had eaten the lion's share.

CHAPTER XVII

SIALACH

Six paddles dipped as one, driving the WAT over the dark water. Overhead the stars dusted a cloudless night sky. The low mounds of Ella and Falarik huddled on the horizon to the south and east. With scarcely a sound we drove the WAT toward the center of the lagoon.

A hundred yards beyond the lagoon shelf I shipped my paddle and let out the plankton net on thirty feet of line. The other paddlers slowed their pace while the fine-meshed cone of gauze strained the water, filtering out the microscopic life and catching it in the bottle at the tip. We towed for five minutes, then reeled in the line. I washed down the net, poured the catch into a large jar, and held this up in the beam of a flashlight.

It was a fine collection. An active crowd of small pale specks cavorted in the beam of light. Copepods darted on erratic courses; their crustacean bodies were too small to make out clearly, but the movements were unmistakable. Slender shrimplike mysids swam among them with graceful movements. Larval fish were there, too, and other things too small to see except as flecks of active white, swimming with restless energy in the bright beam.

The bottle and flashlight passed from hand to hand. Plankton, the small and feebly swimming or drifting life of the sea, is always beautiful to watch in life, and at night in a beam of light it is spectacular. Our few surface hauls in the daytime had taken very little, and Yani, Bakal, and Tachim probably wondered what we thought we were going to catch, towing the silly six-inch net at night. They were much impressed by the crowded mass of active forms, and to their practical minds there quickly came the thought that this was food that baby fish might eat. I shot the net again and we made a second haul, equally as rich.

The WAT skimmed on, and soon we judged we must be near the center of the lagoon. We shipped paddles and drifted to a halt.

Our main purpose tonight was to set out lights and catch the nocturnal swimmers attracted by the glare. We lit the Coleman lanterns and hung these, one over each side, suspended just above the water. Waterproof flashlights were slung with lighted ends submerged. Bob passed out the smaller dipnets and we sprawled on our bellies, heads and arms hanging over the sides. We had chosen a moonless night. Despite the surface reflection from the lanterns, we could see some yards down into the dark green depths below. We watched and waited.

Suddenly there were tiny splashes at the surface, just beyond the rings of light. They hesitated, then moved in, tiny elongate creatures bouncing and skittering over the surface in quick leaps. They were fast, and those we netted seemed taken almost by accident. They proved to be tiny juvenile needlefish (*Strongylura gigantea*), miniatures of those that swam about the patch reefs. We put them into Bob's cans in the center of the boat.

The next arrivals were the silversides (*Pranesus* spp.), larger fishes some five inches long. They clustered in the cones of light below the surface, and we grabbed the larger dipnets and went after them. Tachim burst into an Ifalukian love song as he stood at the edge and swung his net with powerful sweeps. The sound rolled splendidly over the quiet lagoon, doubtless waking babies along the shore. A strong odor of fermented hachi began to drift from his end of the boat. Once, on a long reach, he lost his balance, and the splash sent the fish darting off. He was quickly in the boat again, and the fish back before we had finished laughing.

We had hoped for larger fish. We waited, less and less hopefully as the minutes drifted by. And at last one came, a graceful white shark some four feet long. It circled slowly in the dim light a few yards down, not hunting, just looking, and swam slowly off into the darkness again.

Nothing new arrived. About 11:15 we started for shore, guided by the gleam of lamplight that marked home. We took another rich plankton haul on the way back. At the Fan Nap Ted had the coffee pot going and the cups already on the table.

We had planned to make a night of it. After the coffee, we switched to reef collecting gear and set out across the islet, following the trail from Rolong canoe house toward the windward shore. Low water was not due till 3:00 A.M., but the tide was ebbing, draining the reef flat. We wanted to cover the windward coast, so we split the group, Bob and Ted going north with two of the men, while Tachim, Yani, and myself moved south along the shores of Falalap.

The inner reef flat was rapidly becoming a shallows. We waded across it, and through the deeper trough of the outer flat. The surf rolled in with a resounding boom, but much of the algal ridge was safe enough. In lulls between the larger waves we could work out to the region where the pencil-spined purple sea urchins covered the reef between the surge channels.

I carried the lamp. It cast its circle of brilliance on many things that were uncommon in the daytime. The little Limen (*Acanthurus triostegus*), whitish fish with black zebra stripes along their sides, were everywhere. They seemed sleepy at this hour, drifting lazily on their sides, and were easily speared or taken with a net. Big blue needlefish (*Strongylura gigantea*) moved torpidly in the trough of the outer flat, and we took several of these as well.

The invertebrates were out in force, too. Many were forms that characteristically hid themselves during the day. Armored crustaceans rattled about; here was a curiously flattened scyllarid or squat-lobster (*Parribacus antarcticus*) and there a great dark spider crab, sprouting seaweed fronds from its long legs and pointed carapace. Cowry snails, dark and glistening, crawled about in the open with tentacles protruded, and cone snails hunted meals of worms with teeth-like fine harpoons.

When we had sampled the fauna for science, Tachim sampled it for meat. Taking a flashlight and dipnet in one hand and a long machete in the other, he went about chopping down on fishes with the back of the knife point and scooping them into the net. It proved a most effective way of fishing, much easier and faster than spearing by torchlight.

We turned toward home at last. A fish fry would have been a fitting climax for the trip, but we were weary. We made it back to the Fan Nap just as the first roosters began to crow.

Night work is always interesting to the zoologist. City dwellers on visits to the country soon realize that not everything goes quietly to bed at night; country dwellers visiting the city soon find this out, too. The biologist, stumbling sleepily about with his night light, somewhat disrupts the normal nocturnal scheme of things, but he often sees some worthwhile sights.

On another night we seined the turtle grass beds in the lagoon, Ted and I working ahead and splashing to drive fish into the net while Bob and his men dragged the rectangular thirty-foot seine along. Periodically they pulled the net up on the beach and we examined it. We took some goatfish, a few young mullet (*Mugil cephalus*), and numbers of small shrimp. The lower edge of the net, where it dragged the bottom, snared some beautiful green and yellow tectibranch molluscs (*Haminoea*), curious slug-like forms with soft bodies far too large to retreat into their transparent shells.

We worked down the lagoon shore and turned into the channel between Falarik and Falalap. There were stories about this place. The sting rays which ranged freely over the lagoon bottom during the day were said to congregate here in the channel at night. We kept our flashlights pointed into the water in front of us, and probably scuffed our feet enough to scare the stinging Fai clear to the far end. We didn't see a single one. We didn't catch many fish, either.

If fishing was poor in the turtle grass beds and channel, the night life of the lagoon sand flats and patch reefs made up for it. The great eyes of the squirrel fish shone in the flashlight beams like orange headlamps, and the reefs themselves were jeweled with the gleaming eyes of uncounted thousands of hippolytid shrimps (*Saron marmoratus*), peering from the crevices. Auger snails (*Terebra*) with slender pointed shells crawled on the sand, or just below its surface, leaving clear trails behind; burrowing anemones (cerianthids) jerked their rings of slender tentacles into their holes so quickly they seemed to vanish before our eyes; and gray ghost crabs (*Ocypode*) prowled the beaches, sometimes in clouds, stalked eyes raised above their heads.

Our last month of work saw many daylight trips as well. It was on one of these that a matter came up that was to leave a permanent mark on all of us. A morning on the southwestern reef had been followed by a stop at Ella for lunch. After lunch Tachim amused himself by making small figures out of strips of green coconut leaf—the same general sorts of things our children learn to make by folding paper.

First Tachim made a little bird; then Yani, getting into the spirit of things, made a starfish. Other figures followed, and at last Tachim made a quite respectable double-reed horn. It made quite a racket when blown. It reminded us that the only "musical instruments" we had seen previously on the island had been horns made from large shells, and these were really for signalling rather than music.

We fell to talking of native arts on the boat trip home. Marston had long ago noticed that much of the people's artistry was expressed in the design of maremars—wreaths of flowers for personal adornment. It was something that seemed conspicuously neglected in studies on arts of the Pacific, and Marston had often talked, half jokingly, of the pressed maremar collection he was going to make to remedy this. But with all of our other projects he never even got around to a very systematic job of photographing wreaths.

Another art, which hadn't been so neglected, was tattooing. Many of Ifaluk's men and women, and even some of the children, had tattoo marks here and there. Often these included their names, put on in the Japanese time. A few of the older men were nearly covered with carefully applied native designs, among them Tom and Yani's father Wetriliar. Some of the others bore designs that might have dated back to the German times; still others had a sort of rising sun emblem on the shoulder. And many of the men had handsome long lines of leaping porpoises tattooed along their legs.

I had had an eye on these porpoises for some time, had in fact

come far enough from some of my own inhibitions to admire and even
envy them. The designs were stylized, and seemed a nice compromise
between the primitive touch and clean modern design. I mentioned
my feeling to Ted Bayer.

He looked me in the eye. "I'll get a set if you will," he said. There
was a short silence. Then Yani, in a polite way, began to egg me on.
He thought it was a swell idea. It just so happened that the art of
tattooing was another of his accomplishments, and he'd be glad to
decorate me with a set of porpoises anytime. Tachim enthusiastically
agreed to help out, and after that there was no backing down.

Yani explained the process; usually a mixture of soot and water was
used as ink, and bamboo splinters served as needles. No, he said, on
questioning, it didn't hurt much.

Word got around, and a fair crowd of friends and neighbors followed Yani the next evening, when he showed up ready for the job.
He felt there was no point in using bamboo as long as we had some
steel needles around. He borrowed three needles from Bob, and tied
them together in a row, points all at the same level. He hadn't been
able to locate much soot, but he had brought along a small piece of
Japanese inkstone, which he said was just as good. Rubbed up with a
bit of water from our rainbarrel it made a fine blue-black ink.

I sprawled on the floormats, where the light from the Coleman
lantern was good. We picked a spot about halfway up my right thigh
and trimmed off the hair with scissors. Tachim dipped a strip of coconut leaflet midrib in the ink and laid in the porpoise design carefully. When the audience approved the outlines, Yani dipped his
needles in the ink and began jabbing the points into the skin along
these lines. I could feel the pricks, but they weren't particularly pain-
ful. Yani worked along the outlines first. The audience commented
freely: "A little more here," "straighten this line a bit," and so on. At
last Tachim swabbed off the excess ink, and we all had a critical look.
Yani made a few final adjustments in the outlines, then filled in the
spaces between the lines solidly with blue. Another swabbing, and he
was done. He took the leg and squeezed the area by pulling the skin
away on either side till little drops of tissue fluid appeared like sweat

over the tattoo. The area was swollen a bit, and Yani advised me to sleep on it that night, and not to swim for a day.

I looked over Yani's handiwork, enormously pleased with the result. It was perfectly clear that what I had needed all my life was a trio of Micronesian porpoises tattooed on my leg. Yani had done an excellent job. Marston would turn green with envy when he saw it, I thought, as I smeared the tattooed area liberally with antibiotic ointment.

Ted and Bob had watched the process carefully. I think they probably kept a closer eye on my face than they did on the work itself. Since I hadn't hollered during the process, they felt it couldn't have been very unpleasant. Ted scheduled his tattoo for the next evening, and Bob for a later time. The process was much the same in both cases, though Bob asked for, and got, a slightly larger set of porpoises than either Ted or I.

The activity turned out to have unforseen but favorable effects in our public relations. People admired the tattoos wherever we went, and more than once the women of a household pointed with surprise and delight and burst into sudden Ifalukian love song when they saw the marks. The population knew our time was drawing short, and recognized the sentiments involved in this symbolic identification of ourselves with the island. We were closer to them now than we had been before, and when we left, we would carry a bit of Ifaluk with us for a lifetime.

My sense of time and urgency, though a bit rusty, seemed to be recovering as the days remaining grew fewer. Things went on at the usual rate but we worked later in the evenings, and thoughts ran more to the completion of old projects than to starting new ones. Still, there was one I wanted to try—a census of the Rahom or land crabs (*Cardiosoma*) on Falalap islet. Marston and I had eaten them and seen the females spawn, but we had no real idea of their numbers.

The land crabs burrowed in the ground almost everywhere. Yani and I thought we could recognize Rahom holes when we saw them, and we hoped we'd be able to distinguish occupied burrows from old abandoned holes. An accurate census was out of the question, but by counting holes in sample plots here and there we thought we might make a rough estimate of the total population.

Armed with four six-foot poles we started down Falalap's windward trail, periodically veering to the side, laying the poles in a square, and counting the holes thus framed. The sampling was not truly random, for in some places the dense vegetation and irregular terrain made work impossible. In the forest between boulder ridge and swamp we averaged some twenty-two holes per 100 square feet, though the numbers dropped sharply around the bases of trees with dense root systems. About half the holes looked currently occupied. On the boulder ridge we found only some ten holes to 100 square feet, but the holes here were harder to spot, and the counts less dependable.

It began to sprinkle as we worked down toward the southern end of the bwol. There were many small crab holes in the mud near the edges, but no large ones. Yani said the big crabs did not burrow here, though they often went into the swamp at dusk to eat the young taro plants.

The sky opened up in earnest. We made umbrella hats by putting two big pulach leaves together, base to base, but they weren't much help when we squatted down to count the crab holes. A big pandanus tree stood a few yards away, and under its drooping crown the stones and soil looked fairly dry. We ducked under the fringe of saw-toothed leaves and leaned up against the prop roots at the base of the trunk. Outside the ground shimmered in the downpour.

We spoke casually of this and that, and in no time the subject of women came up. Yani had decided at last to tell me the "funny story" of the girl who had sailed away to Woleai.

I should say here that, while my friends and colleagues at home may nurture secret doubts, all of us westerners had behaved most circumspectly toward the ladies of Ifaluk. It was expected of us by the Trust Territory administration, by our sponsors, and no doubt by our wives, though mine had tactfully refrained from any parting words of advice. I doubt that Ifaluk cared very much one way or another; within the established rules things were left up to individuals, and discretion was expected. And as far as we could see, Ifaluk's friendly ladies had behaved toward us as if they were so many aunts, sisters, and neighbors at home. Marston had once noted in our Journal, "The dangers, alas, are more from falling coconuts than falling maidens."

Yani started in and it soon became apparent that things were not quite what they had seemed. Ifaluk's women, Yani said, had eyed us at first with some awe. This wore off slowly, and at last a few of the island's unattached women began to consider us with an interest somewhat more than neighborly. It was about this time that we first showed the pictures of our wives and children, and this had a very pronounced ardor-cooling effect. Obviously we were married to grand dames of great attractions and chiefly rank and could have no interest in local girls.

After a while the effects of this wore off, too, and two unmarried women had gone so far as to talk to Yani's wife, Letaweriur, about the possibility of an American sweetheart. And Letaweriur had talked them out of it. Not on any "moral" grounds, interestingly enough, but because we were only temporary residents, and would be going away again. She had argued that it would be foolish to form romantic attachments that must inevitably end in broken hearts when we sailed away.

And the argument had been effective. I gave Letaweriur an "A" in advice to the lovelorn. One of the girls had been a bit discouraged, and had departed for the possibly greener fields of Woleai with the canoes. The other was here on the island, somewhere. As a friend and brother Yani said he would point her out to me someday, but as an Ifaluk gentleman he never got around to it.

The days sped by now, and we officially called a halt to most active field work on the last day of October. Ted's birthday came that night, and we celebrated with a small party. We compared our blue porpoise tattoos, which Yani had put on a couple of weeks before, and decided we would just have to cut holes in all our right pantlegs to show them off to good advantage at home.

Eight days of packing ahead. It seemed incredible that we could have brought or accumulated such a mountain of stuff. The Fan Nap was full; so were the two storage tents, the space under the tent fly, and the general landscape for some distance beyond that. Crates, especially those used for shelves and storage cabinets, must be nailed into shape again, and drums that had rusted had to be painted with addresses that would see them safely across the Pacific. We started in, with that curious mixture of anticipation and reluctance that was to mark most of my thoughts until the Coastguard ship PLANETREE came.

The parties started again. We gave the first one ourselves, inviting the four male chiefs and Tom, and asking them please not to bring food. Some thought went in to planning the meal; it seemed safest to stick to the basic starches, so the main dish was a big kettle of pork and beans, fortified with several cans of vienna sausage. As a side order we put out most of our remaining cans of tuna, "Garangap" on Ifaluk. We would see how this went, before deciding on the rest of the menu.

The chiefs and Tom arrived, and it was with some dismay that we saw them laden with pots and pans of breadfruit, pulach, and taro, and several large bottles of tubwa. Tom explained that the chiefs just wanted to contribute a few trifles to garnish the table; it looked as though they didn't trust our cooking.

The party was a great success. We spread the food and sprawled on the floor mats, eating buffet style. Everyone was hungry, and to our surprise we finished not only the whole pot of beans and sausages, but all the tuna and nearly all the breadfruit and taro as well, along with three cans of dried prunes opened for dessert. At the toothpicking stage, Bob brought out a small hand-viewer and a set of kodachrome slides he had taken in Tahiti, Fiji, and the Tuamotus.

It was a good set of pictures. The houses, people, and vegetation were close enough to Ifaluk's own to seem familiar, yet different enough to excite much comment and discussion. There were constant "Yuk!"s of interest and admiration, and a surprisingly wolf-like series of snorts, whistles, and repetitions of "Haaaannnnah!" at one slide of an attractive Tahitian girl. Unforgettable, too, was little Toroman's reaction to a picture of a six-foot, 200-pound Fijian amazon. He grimaced, and made motions as of the lady picking him up under one arm and walking off with him. Tachim could have done no better, and we all laughed together till the tears came.

There were long moments for thought in those last days. I sat on the lagoon beach one evening, letting the warm wind brush my skin and the wavelets nibble at my toes. Overhead the moon drifted like a luminous medusa in a celestial sea, surrounded by the phosphorescent pinpoints of skyborne *Noctiluca*.

Enjoy it now, I thought; the moon and stars won't change, but the rest of it will soon be gone for you. A few days and a few thousand miles would exchange all this for my family and another set of friends. Already, it seemed, I could hear them: "Have a good trip? How was it? What was it like out there?" People don't expect real answers to these questions. I would probably mouth the usual meaningless words.

What had it been like, really? It was not easy to say, for the realities and fancies of the situation were of such different sorts.

The "objective" realities of the place would not be too hard to portray for others, given time. These were the things we had come to study, and we had found out quite a lot. Someday we would complete a fat monograph on the natural history of the island and its people. It would be full of information—of facts about the island. And it would probably gather dust in scattered scholarly archives. For in the cold clichés and precise phrases of scientific papers the vitality is intellectual; the human warmth, the excitements, joys, and frustrations of the work are all too often gone. The scientist, in my experience, rarely observes and manipulates with the aloof detachment usually attributed to his kind; but at least he tries to keep his personality from becoming an active factor in observation and experiment, and his emotional bias from affecting his data and conclusions. The scientist has a special professional attitude and approach to problems in his field, but he is not a special type of man. Whatever his temperament, and the variations cover a wide range, he has his hopes and fears, his moments of courage and maturity, of cowardice and childishness, of happiness and sorrow, of beauty, of struggle, and of peace.

There is no place in a scientific treatise for such things, but they had been an integral part of Ifaluk, a part of the reality for me. And there were experiences, scenes, impressions, and feelings that would remain with me longer than most of the objective facts.

What was it like? It was the feel of hot sun and warm rain on a naked back; the clean murderous grace of a hunting shark seen below the sea. It was moonlight on the lagoon, and the gleam in Bakal's eye as he wound new tinsel in his hair. It was the sound of surf on the reef, and the voices of women singing in the darkness. It was the wonder of a sudden understanding, the excitement of a new thought, the beauty of the blue coral region, and the strutting pride of a fresh porpoise tattoo. It was a talk with Marston or Yani, a wave from Maroligar, a boisterous laugh from Tachim, and a quaint phrase from Tom. It was coconut palms tossing in the wind, the smell of broiling fish and angorik, and a wreath of fresh flowers around my head.

Adventure? It had been adventure of a sort; a change of setting and of culture, and the adventure one might have had exploring any strange small town and its environs, learning to know its land, its natural history, and its people. The adventure of learning and discovery, of seeing data slowly acquire meaning, of watching naive young thoughts ripen and mature.

Danger? Ifaluk seemed safer than our towns at home; it was so small and circumscribed that one quickly gained the security of belonging. Coconuts fell constantly, but they were no hazard when one had learned to watch for them. Sharks? Less dangerous than automobiles at home. If one wanted to get bitten, it could be easily arranged; it would be simple, too, to get hit by an automobile if one tried. Our adventures, being mostly of the mind, involved few risks, but adventures of the mind can be exciting too. In this materialistic world it sometimes seemed to me that scientific research was the last refuge of the romantic.

I had been fortunate in my companions of the trip. Living closely with others in the field I had come to know them well. Well enough, at any rate, to realize that each was ultimately enigmatic, a unique and mysterious bundle of complexities and contradictions. They were a likeable lot, thoughtful, intelligent men of good will, intensely human even in their shortcomings. They liked their lives and work and laughed easily and often. Their interests took them from the specific to the general, from the example to the principle, and they all liked to talk. It led to some memorable evenings of conversation, starting with relaxed yarns of past experiences and present work, and moving into headier topics like the nature of art, the meaning of "importance," the impact of the individual on history, and man's place in the cosmos. Not that we neglected woman's place there, even in our most egg-headed moments. All in all, the atmosphere had been one of coopera-tive inquiry into nature and man, rather than competitive struggle for individual achievement and gain.

Had the inquiry been successful? We had gained some of our ob-jectives, but by no means all. We had a good picture of the structure of the island, on the surface anyway. Its form was inscribed on maps, its climate tabulated in neat columns of figures. Flora and fauna we had surveyed and collected, more thoroughly in some groups than in others, and by and large we had a fair idea of what was there.

On the ecological side we had plotted the major zones and associa-tions of organisms, pretty crudely in some places, better in others, and we knew the distributions and food habits of some of the commoner things. Our quantitative studies fell far short of my initial hopes, especially on the reefs, but perhaps I had expected too much. Studies of species interrelationships and community dynamics of land and reef were better left for another expedition, when the results of the first had been digested and processed. For a community of organisms, as for an individual organism, physiology and function are better studied when the anatomy is known.

Perhaps we had done best in our attempts to study the natural history of Micronesian man, and ultimately this might be the most useful outcome of the trip. We had found, and tried to measure, the things man used from land and sea. We had assessed the present es-sential needs against present resources and had found a surplus, real or potential, in almost everything except fishes. From the point of view of agricultural crops and methods, the taro swamps were produc-ing with good efficiency; coconut plantings were somewhat haphazard, but the present yield provided a great surplus over present needs, even with a copra production of some thirty-three tons per year. Bread-fruit supplies were adequate in season. This, with taro and coconuts, all low in proteins, provided the basic diet. The main protein source was fish, and the supply here could not be increased safely and sig-nificantly without increasing the effort to fish the areas beyond the rim of the atoll. We weren't sure whether this would yield additional food proportional to the energy expended, but the prospects didn't look optimistic.

While careful cultivation of food plants at the expense of partly native forest might nevertheless enable Ifaluk to marginally support twice its present population on a low protein diet, there seemed little point in considering this. The real limiting factors here did not normally operate in the atoll's biological economy; they were introduced by the occasional severe storms which swept the island, destroying most of the means of livelihood for man. For a land periodically doomed to start halfway from scratch again, a population pushing hard against Malthusian limits could only suffer larger scale disasters.

Local housing seemed ideally suited to the climate, much more so than western dwellings of boards and corrugated iron that could turn to ovens in the tropic sun. Thatched roofs might not last as long, but the raw materials were free and easy to prepare, and the thatch provided a fine insulation and shelter.

Local clothing (or the absence of it) too, seemed ideally suited to the local needs. We hoped that the people of Ifaluk would have the integrity and fortitude to withstand the well-meant but, to us, essentially evil-minded attempts of outsiders to dress them in suits and Mother Hubbards. Western dress was unpleasantly hot here; it would surely prevent evaporation of sweat and encourage fungus skin infections; it would probably decrease bathing, and would make the use of the lagoon bathroom difficult and impractical unless all people were educated to use the benjos. Certainly we hoped that there would be no attempts to supplement the lagoon benjos with land privies; excreting into the sea seemed far and away the best means of preventing the spread of diseases and human parasites.

In many ways, then, the island seemed better off now than it might be with the introduction of analagous items and methods of the West. Which was only reasonable; after all, the people here had had a good many centuries in which to learn pleasant and successful ways of doing things on the island.

On the other hand, there was certainly room for some improvement, assuming the present way of life would continue for a time with only a relatively slow change. It seemed very likely, for example, that something might be done about the flies and mosquitoes. Nobody liked the pests, and perhaps a periodic spraying of the atoll by airplanes might eventually be feasible. In the meantime, more mosquito nets would certainly help reduce the problem.

As for diet, Ifaluk wanted more meat. Eventually imports of canned meat would increase, but for a starter it looked as though the island might well try to increase its pig population. The food for them was already there; pigs were fed the same basic starches as man, supplemented by the entrails of fishes and leaves of half a dozen species of common plants. And the introduction of a hardy tobacco, if such were available, would do much to relieve the periodic shortages that made most adults unhappy.

As time went on, Ifaluk would probably follow the pattern of change of many another Pacific island. Conversion to Christianity would surely come. Further contact with the outer world would increase the desire for things not locally available. Even now, Ifaluk wanted cotton cloth, metal knives and tools, lamps and kerosene, tobacco, matches, mosquito nets, pots and pans, fishhooks and line, perfume and face paint, a bit of western food, and such. Someday, radios and sewing machines would be in demand, too.

As with most small Pacific islands, copra, the dried kernel of the ripe coconut, was almost the only thing available in quantity that could be exported with reasonable profit. Assuming the soap for which the coconut oil was used would not be replaced entirely by modern detergents, the people here would probably turn gradually to the more systematic production of copra. Here, as on other islands, the cultivation of taro in the swamps would probably decline as the land there, and in the partly native forest, was planted more heavily in coconuts. It doesn't seem likely that Ifaluk will work too hard at copra production; the people place too high a value on their leisure time to take up any regular work beyond that necessary for a living and a few extras. But as more goods become available, and present luxuries slowly become necessities, more copra will surely be made and sold.

It seemed to us that there were other things that could be exported, too. Native woven skirts, hand-carved bowls, wooden paint-pots carved in the form of birds, model canoes—these things would be much admired by our friends at home. A worthwhile project might well be the discovery of limited outlets for such goods in specialty shops, such as the gift shops of art and natural history museums. The latter were already doing a good business selling plaster casts of sculptures and wood carving from odd parts of the world. Handicrafts and weaving might provide, in time, as much income as copra-making, and at tasks at least as congenial.

Other changes would come about, too. Eventually Ifaluk would have western medical care available in the form of a well-trained medical practitioner with good facilities. This would no doubt add to the population problem eventually, as it had over much of the rest of the world, but that was no justification for doing without it.

Someday, perhaps in the near future, Ifaluk would have a resident teacher who did some real teaching. With increased contacts with the West, a knowledge of English and of western business, politics, and religion would be essential if the islanders were to preserve the degree of cultural and political integrity they desired for themselves. Knowledge was strength, potentially at least, and would be necessary for self-protection against exploiters and those desiring to impose changes from without. A teacher might maintain weather and population records for the atoll, and when Radio Ifaluk really got going, he might serve as an effective link between the island and the outer world. These suggestions did not originate with us; already the Trust Territory was trying to improve medicine and education with these things in mind, and on the larger and less isolated islands progress in this direction was already significant.

As contact with the West increased, as demand for trade goods went up, it seemed inevitable that there would come about a loss of self-sufficiency, and an increasing dependence on the outer world. It seemed too bad in a way, but perhaps this was sentiment speaking. We admired the proud, independent, self-sufficient islanders as we admired our own pioneers and frontier settlers of earlier days. Soon Ifaluk would no longer lie on western civilization's "frontier." And a part of becoming "civilized," in the western sense at least, involves becoming dependent on a lot of other people in other places. It goes hand in hand with an acceptance of the industrial and technological revolutions, and we ourselves have not regarded it as evil. Whether it made life richer was a moot question, but it certainly made it more comfortable. I have no doubt that our own visit to the island helped speed the changes to come, for it gave people a look at lots of things they had not realized they wanted before.

Eventually there would be emigration, if the pattern here followed that of the Polynesian islands, and perhaps with this, overpopulation might not become a problem. Already there were a few young men, Yani among them, who wanted to see the world beyond the western Carolines. As contacts increased and opportunities arose, the younger and more adventurous would leave, as they did everywhere else, heading for the larger islands, bigger towns, and eventually the continents. One distinguished Pacific anthropologist foresaw in this trend, and in improvements in transportation and communication, a steady decline in population on the islands through emigration. And perhaps, he speculated, the south sea islands may ultimately become transformed into a series of island playgrounds and resorts for continental peoples, the remaining local inhabitants catering to the guest and tourist industry. Perhaps it will come to that; if so, I hope it will be well after my time. An alternative might be the rise, eventually, of a self-administered state, with its Fagoliers and Maroligars sitting in a Congress of Micronesia, regulating their own destinies at last after the overlords of Yap, Spain, Germany, Japan, and America have come and gone.

INDEX

Adoption, 43-44
Age count, 34
Agriculture, 74-75, 109-10, 112, 114
Akers, Ernestine, 17
Alcohol, use of, 77, 121-22
Atolls, 157, 202-19

Boondocks, 41-42
Breadfruit, 72-74, 108
Burrows, Edwin, 15

Canoe houses, 41
Census, 27-31, 34
Chiefs, 53, 55, 57, 62, 68-69, 227, 230-34
Childbearing, 34-35
Children, treatment of, 30-31, 43-44
Christianity (on Pacific islands), 28, 93, 171-72, 174-75
Clams, giant, 88-89
Coconut trees, 75-77, 108
Cook, James (Captain), 173
Coolidge, Harold, 14, 202
Copra, 33, 95, 126
Coral reefs, 60, 86-87, 90-91, 184, 202-19; structure, 209-12

Crabs: land, 99-103, 241-42; coconut, 114-15

Dancing, 51, 64, 66-67, 69-70, 81, 83-85
Darwin, Charles, 163, 214-16
Diet, 71-72, 229-30, 247, 249
Disease, 31, 35-36, 56, 132

Eggs, 78-79, 143, 145

Fan Nap, 20, 25-26
Fishes, 85-91, 187-95, 225-28, 235-39
Fishing, 46-47, 59-64, 188-91, 235-39; weapons, 46-47; by net, 60-61, 63-64
Flies, 19, 20, 57
Food, 70-80, 98-99, 229-30, 247-49

German influence, 36, 180-84
Government, by chiefs, 53, 55, 57, 62, 68-69, 227, 230-34

Health, 31, 34, 35-36, 56, 71-72, 132, 185
Heyerdahl, Thor, 38
History of Ifaluk, 173-86
Household system, 42-43
Houses, structure of, 29-30

Japanese influence: on Ifaluk, 36, 114, 115, 139, 184-85; on Pacific Islands, 58, 84, 197
Jesuit influence, 171-73

Lagoons, 147-73
Land ownership, 42-43
Lizards, 115-16, 195-200; kinds, 197-98; catching of, 198-200
Lütke, Fedor, 178-79

Mapping, 39-42, 44-46, 86-87, 113, 141
Marriage, 117-18
Menstruation taboos, 28-29, 35
Micronesians, 37-38, 62-63
Modesty, 30, 117
Mosquitoes, 57

Navigation, by islanders, 52-54, 220, 224-25

Octopus, 89
Ornamentation, 239; male, 64-66; tattooing, 239-41

Pacific Islands: interest in, 15-16; population decline, 35-36; navigation in, 52-54, 220, 224-25; history of, 168-86
Pacific Science Board, 14, 15, 17, 202
Physical aspect of inhabitants, 140-41; age count, 34; size, 36-37; racial characteristics, 37-38
Polynesians, 37-38, 62-63
Population, of Ifaluk, 34
Population decline, 34-36

Racial characteristics, 37-38
Rainfall, 130, 134-36
Rats, 115-16

Reefs, 60, 86-87, 90-91, 184, 202-19; structure of, 209-12
Religion, 26, 28, 81-83, 93
Rotenone, 190

Sand, 154-55, 162-63
Sarfeit, Ernst, 183-84
Schooling, 45
Sea-cucumber, 88, 206-07
Sex habits, 117-18
Sharks, 47-48, 60, 158-59
Size, of inhabitants, 36-37
Smoking, habit, 50-51, 95-96
Songs, 84, 118-20, 146, 182-83, 223-24
Spanish influence, 171-73
Spiro, Melford, 15
Spoehr, Alex, 14

Taro, 74-75
Tattooing, 239-41
Tides, 159-62
Tobacco, use of, 50-51, 95-96
Trade goods, 96-97, 126-27, 184
Turtle grass, 150-52
Typhoon, 26-27, 31-33, 183-84; of 1907, 33, 36, 140, 141

Vegetation, 106-14; origin on Ifaluk, 107-09

Water, study of, 23, 132-39, 143-46, 206; wells, 105-06, 112, 143-44, 146; rainfall, 130, 134-36; pools, 136-37; tides, 159-62
Weather, 26-27, 31-33
Wilson, James, 173-76
Women, 63, 66-67, 119-20, 223-24, 242-43; menstruation taboos, 28-29, 35; childbearing, 34-35; work, 75, 112-13; dancing, 84